**Nicola Owen** is th................................ marketing company. She lives in...

**Sydney Higgins**, Nicola's co-writer, has published many books including a biography of Sir Henry Rider Haggard and an edition of Rider Haggard's diaries. He collaborated with actor Tony Booth on his autobiography, and with Ed Punchard on his account of the Piper Alpha disaster. He and his wife, Anna, live in Italy.

# NICOLA

## Nicola Owen
**with Sydney Higgins**

## CORGI BOOKS

NICOLA
A CORGI BOOK 0 552 13946 7

Originally published in Great Britain by Bantam Press,
a division of Transworld Publishers Ltd

PRINTING HISTORY
Bantam Press edition published 1992
Corgi edition published 1993

Set in 10pt Linotype Plantin by
Photoprint, Torquay, Devon

Corgi Books are published by Transworld Publishers Ltd,
61–63 Uxbridge Road, Ealing, London W5 5SA, in Australia by
Transworld Publishers (Australia) Pty Ltd, 15–25 Helles Avenue,
Moorebank, NSW 2170, and in New Zealand by Transworld
Publishers (NZ) Ltd, 3 William Pickering Drive, Albany,
Auckland.

Printed and bound in Great Britain by
Cox & Wyman Ltd, Reading, Berks.

# Acknowledgements

I would like to thank the following people:

Syd Higgins for the endless hours and painstaking care he has devoted to my story and his wife Anna for her support in this task.

Andrew Best of Curtis Brown, for his understanding and patience.

Dr Katharina Dalton for helping me live a normal life again. I hope this book makes a significant contribution towards her lifelong work.

Sally and Johnnie for putting up with me during these difficult years and for never allowing me to feel guilty over all the hurt I must have caused them.

And, finally, my parents for their unwavering persistence that meant they never gave up on me. This book would never have been written without them.

*Apart from Dr Dalton the names of the professionals who appear in this book have been changed. Nicola Owen appreciates that their advice was given during confidential discussions and felt that it was appropriate to protect their identity.*

# Contents

# Foreword

This is a true and harrowing tale of a young teenager's bizarre change of behaviour on reaching adolescence, and of her parents' unremitting search for a cure. Nicola had a happy childhood in a loving family, but something went drastically wrong at puberty when she became an unpredictable and violent female prone to self-mutilation and arson.

I became involved in Nicola Owen's case when Nicola's parents, Pam and Ed Owen, came to see me because they had heard of my research into premenstrual syndrome. They had become convinced that their daughter's behaviour was connected with her menstrual cycle and asked me to examine her in Holloway Prison.

PMS may be defined as the recurrence of symptoms (of which there are over 150 as diverse as asthma, epilepsy, sinusitis and the most frequent, and most distressing, psychological changes) which always occur a few days before menstruation starts followed by normality once bleeding has ceased.

I have been working on cases of PMS, first with the endocrinologist, Dr Raymond Greene, and subsequently in my own practice, since the inception of progesterone therapy in 1948. At that time, however, the medical illness, premenstrual syndrome (PMS), was virtually unknown although the psychiatric illness, premenstrual tension (PMT), had been recorded. Interestingly, psychiatric treatments do little for PMS cases, whereas progesterone treatment will successfully treat both PMS and PMT.

My own research gradually and painstakingly built up a picture of the effects of the menstrual cycle on women of all ages; and this provided the background on which Nicola Owen's defence was based.

Nicola's case made legal history in England as the first time in which premenstrual syndrome was used as a mitigating factor in a criminal case. Since 1979 a plea of PMS has been used in court on several occasions in cases of murder, infanticide, manslaughter and a host of other crimes. As in Nicola's story, all the successful cases have been diligently researched and the court presented with factual evidence of the dates of the recurrent offences and dates of menstruation, together with evidence of mental disturbances in the premenstruum and normality after menstruation.

Nicola's case established a precedent in law and also brought about an increased awareness of PMS. Yet still in Britain and throughout the world there remain thousands of 'Nicolas' languishing in prisons and mental hospital wards whose lives could be restored to normality if each one were individually considered, carefully monitored and given the opportunity to have appropriate treatment. One wishes there were more parents like Pam and Ed Owen, whose endless determination and faith in their daughter brought about my own involvement in this case as well as a medical explanation of the mysterious changes in Nicola's character.

Finally, I would like to emphasize the courageous way Nicola faced up to the recognition and full implications of her condition and how she struggled successfully to use her second chance, allowing bygones to be bygones, but ever ready to help others in trouble.

Dr Katharina Dalton
December 1991

# Prologue

It was a grey, cheerless February day. The drizzle rattled warningly against the window panes and, with a low whisper, a cold wind gusted through the conifers. I stared out of my bedroom window at the barren garden, dominated by a giant weeping willow, standing lethargic and isolated in the middle of the sodden lawn. The starkness of the scene was relieved only by the evergreens around the borders of the garden. I remember the day they were planted. It seemed so long ago. Nearer to me, the rose bushes were lifeless and cold. Only a few months ago, they had been a spectacular mass of vivid colour.

I turned away and walked over to the full-length mirror on my bedroom wall. I no longer knew the girl staring back at me. I felt my throat tightening but couldn't cry.

Determined to see exactly how repulsive I really was, I slowly began to undress, until I stood completely naked in front of the mirror. Although I was only seventeen, my body was bloated, obese. My stomach was so swollen that it seemed as though I was pregnant. Even though I was standing with my legs apart, the insides of my thighs still met. Without the support of a bra, my breasts hung so heavily they hurt. My whole body was repellent. Raising my eyes to my face, I hardly recognized myself. The swollen features were accentuated by the brutality of hair shorn to a half-inch crew cut. Her eyes – my eyes – were glazed, but as I looked harder I could see

11

the total despair in them. This person, this creature, was me.

I knew I'd lost everything. Around the mirror were photographs of famous ballerinas I'd admired and who once had inspired my life. Among them were photographs of myself in dancing costumes, winning medals and receiving cups. I looked so happy and content. Above the mirror were some of the best modelling shots that had been taken of me. I heard the voices: 'Oh, Nicola! What a fantastic photograph!', 'You're so lucky to have such a beautiful face!', 'Nick, you've got a terrific figure!', 'Believe me, Nicola, you've got everything it takes to be the second Shirley MacLaine!'

I lifted my hands to my head. I couldn't bear it. What had gone wrong? What had caused this terrible self-destruction? How I hated my life. How I hated being unable to do anything about it. Even if I'd had sufficient strength of character to sew up the seams of my life, I wouldn't have known where to begin. Everything was in tatters.

Deep in my stomach, there was a hollow, empty feeling. No more pain – I couldn't fight it any more. I'd come to the end. I wanted to do something so vicious to myself. I had no thoughts about other people. I just so hated the person in the mirror. I really wanted to hurt her. I really wanted to kill her. I knew that meant I was going to die. But I knew I wanted to die. In a few moments, I'd be at peace.

Knowing that I was alone in the house, I walked purposefully downstairs. I didn't bother to take a last look around. So much an expression of my parents and their successes, the house was all too familiar to me. I'd spent almost all the seventeen years of my life there. I searched the lounge until I found what I was looking for. Then I returned slowly upstairs to my bedroom.

It had only recently been redecorated and refurbished. The pretty pink and green flowered wallpaper matched my eiderdown. The bed's old-fashioned brass headrail complemented the brass chair by the dressing-table. The white paint of the wardrobe's louvred doors contrasted with the deep fresh green of the carpet. There was the little wooden rocking-chair where I'd sat reading for hours on end. I'd chosen the decor myself and so I'd always felt happy and relaxed there. It overlooked the garden which backed on to the woods and, in the spring, a cherry tree's branches, laden with blossom, framed the window.

I knew that what I was about to do was wrong, but I was so desperate it was the only way left open to me. I felt my mind had become twisted and evil. There seemed to be two Nicolas – one good and one bad. There's no hope for you any more, I told myself. You're mad, you're evil, you're sick and I don't care about you any more. I'm not going to fight for you ever again.

Now I watched as I began to destroy everything, powerless to prevent what was happening. I opened the box of matches, took one out, struck it and it went out. The next match didn't seem to have any effect. So I lit a third and held the flickering light to the curtains until the flames began to dance through the pink roses. I watched, horrified at what I was doing, and yet I remained standing there, staring at the blazing curtains.

Blankly, I walked over to my bed and lay down. The room was rapidly filling with black smoke. The entire run of curtains was ablaze. The fire was devouring everything and the heat was becoming unbearable. Even though I was still naked, my whole body was bathed in perspiration.

Hearing a sudden sound at the bedroom door, I turned my head to see Emma, our nine-week-old puppy, looking at me with large, brown, terrified eyes. She started to bark and then to whine. I shouted at her to go away, 'Emma, get out! Leave me alone!' But she wouldn't.

A loud crack resounded through the room, followed by a cascade of shattering glass. The entire area by the window was a mass of flames that would soon envelop the entire room.

13

'Oh, my God! What have I done now?'

I began to cry.

Emma's whining suddenly broke into a high-pitched bark. I jumped off the bed and pulled on a large, baggy, black jumper. I'd just had time to grab my plimsolls when a piece of burning timber crashed on to the bed. Sweeping Emma into my arms, I raced downstairs. She tried to struggle free because I was holding her so tightly, but I couldn't risk her running back into the fire.

I opened the door to my father's office and, picking up the telephone, dialled the emergency number. 'Operator! There's a fire! . . . What? . . . It's number thirty-six Camden Road, Bexley . . . My name's Nicola Owen. Please come quickly. The whole house is burning!'

As I replaced the receiver, I heard a sharp tapping on the window. Anxiously peering in was a sandy-haired man in his mid-thirties who I recognized as our next-door neighbour.

I turned away and walked out of the office and back into the hall. There was the acrid smell and fierce crackling roar of burning. As I looked up the stairs, swirling black smoke was ominously edging its way downwards.

Emma was still struggling frantically and whining in sheer terror. I held her firmly with both arms and sat down at the foot of the stairs, staring ahead of me at the shelf above the radiator. It was full of little ornaments of children sitting in apple trees, playing with kittens and feeding chickens. They were all smiling at me. I could almost hear their spluttering laughter as if I'd played a successful joke on them.

It all had to be a terrifying nightmare. Any second, I'd wake up and everything would be as it always was.

Suddenly, I became aware of the doorbell's persistent ringing. Automatically, I got up and opened the front door. As I did so, I heard the distant sound of sirens and clashing bells rapidly coming closer . . .

# CHAPTER ONE

## *A Happy Family*

It was a balmy June evening. Dappled sunlight played on the rippling surface of the narrow stream that meandered along the bottom of Bexley Woods.

Ed Owen was strolling up and down the bank, carefully monitoring his two young daughters as they trawled the clear water with their tiny fishing-nets. Nearest to him was Nicola – the elder of the two by some nineteen months. She was a thin, delicate-looking six year old with enormous blue eyes. As she stood in the middle of the stream, the water gently sloshed over the top of her rubber boots.

'I've got one, Dad! I have! I have!' Nicola suddenly shouted, gazing rapturously at her tangled fishing-net as it visibly jerked.

Ed was as excited as Nicola. 'Bring the net over to the jar, Nicola,' he said calmly but authoritatively, 'and carefully turn it inside out.'

Weighed down by her water-filled boots, Nicola struggled to the bank and did as her father had instructed. She squealed with delight as a small fish plopped from the fishing-net into the jar.

'Look, Daddy. Look, look!' she exclaimed. 'I've really caught a fish!'

'You've caught a stickleback, Nicola.'

'A stiggleback?'

'No. Stickle. Stickle-back. That's what that fish is called.'

'I've caught a stickleback, Sally,' Nicola shouted to her younger sister, who was fishing a little further downstream.

'Shush, Nicola. Keep quiet,' Sally replied bossily as she stared intently into the stream. She quickly jerked her net towards a fish and then angrily bellowed, 'Oh, it's gone. It's all your fault, Nicola, for making such a noise. You made me lose my fish!'

Ed laughed at Sally's typical display of temper and then told both of them it was time to pack up and return home. Sally wanted to stay until she too caught a fish. Nicola, as always, obeyed immediately. She couldn't wait to get home to show the stickleback she had caught to her mother and Johnnie, her baby brother.

Efficient as always, Ed soon had everything under control. Lizzie, the family's pet Dalmatian, was summoned back from her scampering hunt through the woods and the fishing tackle was gathered together. The two little girls, who'd been immaculate in their matching cotton dresses when they'd set off a couple of hours earlier, were both sopping wet as, hand-in-hand with their father, they trudged up the steep stony path that led through the woods towards their home.

The Owen family lived at 36 Camden Road – an imposing, detached house that was new when they moved in. At the rear, the beautiful garden Ed and Pam's father had painstakingly converted from a vast expanse of bare clay, sloped gently down to meet the ancient oaks of Bexley Woods. Conifers had been planted around the large central lawn which would soon be dominated by the burgeoning weeping willow. By the house, there was an attractive patio and the nearby pond was fed by a trickling waterfall that was floodlit at night.

After racing up the crazy-paving drive, Nicola and Sally burst noisily into the kitchen, each eager to tell their mother about the afternoon's adventure. Usually, there was no contest. Sally was far more demanding and talkative than her shy and somewhat withdrawn elder sister but this time Nicola had an obvious advantage. It was she who had caught the tiny fish that was swimming aimlessly about inside the glass jar.

Pam Owen was glad of the chance to praise Nicola. Although she had much more in common with Sally, whose effervescent personality was similar to her own, Pam felt closer to and more loved by Nicola. She was such a good girl, never making a fuss about anything, not even her many illnesses. There was something about her elder daughter that made her seem so very vulnerable.

Nicola somehow reminded Pam of Ed as he had been when they first met. Although then he had been working in the City as a trainee accountant, he seemed slightly out of place among his fellow bowler-hatted commuters. This was partly due to his solidly respectable working-class background but it also stemmed from the inner uncertainties Pam detected lurking beneath his obvious charm, intelligence and fierce determination that amounted almost to brashness.

With her own remarkable inner strength, Pam provided Ed with constant support and encouragement. Whenever he was down, she would urge him, 'Come on, Eddie, be strong. Let's get to the top.' And that's what they were doing. Having qualified as an accountant, Ed was to establish what would quickly become his own extremely successful management consultancy. Tall, slim and athletic, he and his pretty blonde wife were an attractive couple.

They both enjoyed being parents, consciously putting their family first and working hard to create a happy home. With no sign of the dark clouds gathering beyond the clear horizon, their obvious successes made them feel pleasantly smug. Whenever a friend said, 'You just don't realize how lucky you are,' they were wont to think, it's not luck. We've worked for this. You only get out of life what you put into it and children are only what their parents bring them up to be.

* * *

I had an incredibly happy childhood. Sally, Johnnie and I always had the feeling we were really loved. It seemed that we had whatever we wanted and Mum and Dad made everything such fun. In some ways, perhaps, we were spoiled.

I was five when we moved into the house at Camden Road. It was really spacious and each of us had our own room. Mum used to get excited about the décor and every room was beautifully furnished, mostly in the cottage-like style she insisted on calling 'chintz'. Sally's and my bedrooms were done in exactly the way we wanted them. We helped choose everything – the colour scheme and even what we wanted for our bedspreads. It was all exciting and, like everything else, we did it together as a family.

As children, we were given every possible advantage when it came to education. All three of us were privately educated up to the age of eleven. Sally and I then went to the local girls' grammar school and Johnnie attended boarding-school.

Looking back, we had so many good times when I was a child. We had spectacular parties. Mum and Dad worked for days arranging everything. Then, when our friends arrived, Dad organized and refereed all the games. Mum gave out the prizes and handed round the beautifully presented food she had prepared. Her birthday cakes were fantastic.

Even the weekends were made special. Every Sunday, we went to a different place, all over the countryside. We used to pick blackberries, play games, go for long walks, sit down to have a huge picnic supper and then, absolutely tired out from all our exploring, return home. It was always so much fun.

Mum and Dad also used to let us have animals. Our first family pet was Lizzie, our Dalmatian, and we had her from a little puppy. Her mother had actually been a champion at Crufts, but to us she was the special friend we would take for long walks around the local wood. We also had many cats, because we often felt sorry for some stray and took it in. Then we started getting interested in gerbils, but they were always being eaten by the cat or squashed because somebody had let one of them out of their cage. The gerbil stage was all pretty traumatic and at the end of the garden there was a growing line of little graves for all the gerbils that had died. Having so many animals at different times was, I suppose, all part of being young.

Some of the loveliest memories I have are of our holidays. When I was seven, we started going abroad each year – to Italy, Spain or France. Sometimes, we would stay in a villa, other times we would camp. Dad was always able to create a great sense of adventure. We have camped high up in the Pyrénées and all five of us have spent the night together in the car. It all seemed so exciting.

The packing for these holidays would take days. All the bedrooms looked like dry-cleaners as dresses, skirts, blouses and shirts of every description hung from every possible ledge, window sill, door knob or wall light. The assorted suitcases would be gradually filled with an apparently endless flow of freshly ironed clothing, each layer being carefully protected with sheets of tissue paper.

Inevitably, on the day before we were due to leave, Mum would announce, 'We won't get everything in, Ed.'

Then Dad would be despatched to buy the extra suitcase. Mum would specify the correct size and colour – the colour of things was always important to her. After the holidays, the ever growing collection of suitcases would spend the rest of the year stowed away in the loft.

Even so, there always seemed to be some snorkel, flipper, pair of sandals or deflated beach ball that had been left out.

'I've got an idea, Ed,' Mum would say. 'Why don't you use the beach bag for those things?'

'Good idea. Go and get it.'

'I've packed it, actually.'

'That's absolutely great, Pam. Just great. Which case is it in?'

'I think it's in that one!'

'Did you say "think"? Tell you what! You unpack and find the beach bag and I'll go and make some tea.'

'We could buy another beach bag.'

'I didn't hear that!'

On the morning we were to set off, Dad would come into our bedrooms and wake us up at five o'clock. We'd put on really warm clothes and clamber into the car, which was laden inside and on the roof-rack with camping equipment, food and clothing. By the time we'd reached the ferry, we'd be bursting with excitement. Mum used to buy us what we called our boating-outfits with a very English kind of sailor-look about them. After crossing the Channel, we'd motor all the way down through France. Whenever we became bored, we'd stop and get out the camping stove to make ourselves tea. Mum would cook something to eat and it was all part of the great adventure. Back in the car, we'd sing together and tell jokes until we arrived.

One year, Dad pitched our blue and orange tent in the shade of some ancient pines on the beach near St Tropez. Every morning we'd breakfast on sliced melons and peaches with bowls of cereal and long-life milk brought with us from England. One evening, after we'd eaten at an open-air restaurant, we discovered that the car had disappeared. Dad found it had been towed away to a police compound and we all watched in amazement as he stealthily crept in and stole back his car. We weren't told till later that, by that time, Dad knew he was free to collect the car and so, for the rest of the holiday, every time he saw a policeman, he'd duck down beneath the steering-wheel gasping, 'Mustn't let them see me!'

We were a real family. Everything we did was always together. Each Christmas was a special, magical time, because we all used to believe in Father Christmas until we were about ten years old. On Christmas Eve, all the grandparents would come over to help us hang our big pillow-cases in the lounge by the fireplace. Then we'd pour Santa a sherry and leave him three mince pies. Grandad would be in the kitchen, plucking the turkey. Nanny would be baking mince-pies and Dad, who always had a great sense of occasion, would play a recording of carols. Everybody really enjoyed themselves and afterwards it was difficult to sleep.

At five in the morning, we'd run downstairs and open all our presents. Then we'd wake everybody else up, desperate to show them what Father Christmas had brought us. At midday, we'd sit down to a lavish dinner. The table was elegantly laid – all the silver was out, the best linen, beautiful candles and the most expensive crackers Mum could buy. It was a very, very happy time for the whole family.

I was always very close to Sally, my sister, although I can remember that she was the one everyone thought was really pretty and sweet. She was very elfin-like and was always the centre of attention wherever we went. I was a bit gawky, skinny and spotty, and I felt much more ill at ease with strangers than Sally did. She used to know what to say to the adults to amuse them and she'd happily clamber all over them. She says now that she's been aware of the opposite sex since she was four years old. Perhaps it was because of this that, when we were young, it was always Sally who was in the limelight. But we used to play a lot when we were alone together. One of our games was called 'Sally and Nicola'. I'd pretend I was Sally and she would pretend to be me. She'd put all her belongings in my bedroom and I'd put all mine in hers.

I suppose it was because I was five years older than Johnnie that I wasn't as close to him as I was to Sally, but I really loved him. He was so handsome and cute. Sally and I used to have a race into his bedroom every morning to see who could be the first to cuddle him. But, when he was two or three, I used to be a bit spiteful with him. If nobody was watching, I'd pinch him to make him cry so I could then become all sweet and cuddle him.

As a child, I was very shy and withdrawn. I was also painfully thin, very round-shouldered and rather sickly. When I was about four, I began to suffer from infantile eczema behind my knees and in the creases of my arms. If I had a cold, it tended to develop into a severe bronchial cough. I often seemed to be ill when there was about to be any special event.

When I was six, I started having asthma attacks which usually occurred if I was nervous or worried about something. My parents were really very good about this and didn't make a big thing of it. Dad would put me in bed, open all my bedroom windows and say things like, 'Do you know, Nick, why I planted all those conifers out there?'

'No!' I'd gasp.

'Because conifers give off a special kind of tree-oxygen! As you're breathing in, try and smell it coming off the trees and in a few minutes you'll be fine.'

In addition to my recurring illnesses, I was also very accident-prone. Once, when I was cleaning my teeth, I burst a blood vessel. Several times I was sent to hospital – once to have my adenoids out because I'd had so many severe sore throats. On another occasion, when Mum and Dad were out and a baby-sitter was looking after us, I did what I'd often seen Dad doing. I used a razor-blade to cut open a nearly empty bottle of the soothing lotion for my eczema so I could get out the last few drops. Unfortunately, the blade slipped and I severed two tendons and a cartilage in my left index finger.

At about this time, I went to see Sally in a dancing display. She was dressed up as a piglet and was doing a little routine. As I watched her on stage, I thought, I want to dance. So I told Mum and she said, 'Lovely. I'll take you to dancing classes.' Everybody, including the doctor, thought it was a good idea and so I started dancing. I wasn't exceptional at first, but I worked very hard and really enjoyed it.

Shortly afterwards, Sally gave up dancing. Although she's very temperamental and lazy, she's riddled with talent and is extremely musical. Dad's a bit of a party pianist and so he was delighted when Sally started to play the piano. Eventually, she was to win a place at the Royal Academy of Music.

Although I quite liked school, my school reports began to suggest that my work wasn't as good as it ought to have been. When I was nine, I was taken to have my eyes tested and the optician frightened the life out of my parents by announcing, 'There's something seriously wrong with Nicola's eyes.'

Dad then took me to a top ophthalmist in London. When Dad asked him how bad my eyes were, he said, 'Well, Mr Owen, if I was to hold five fingers up at arm's length from her, she couldn't see them.' When Dad asked me how I'd managed to read words on the blackboard in the classroom, I told him that I always went to the front to ask the teacher a question so I could see what she'd written. After that, I began to wear spectacles and my school work improved dramatically.

Dancing was very good for me and I loved it. As well as increasing my confidence, it improved my posture and I suffered far less from wheezy colds. I also discovered that I was quite good at it. I began to be entered for examinations and one after another I passed them with honours – the highest possible mark.

Yet I suppose that all my accidents, illnesses and operations had made me very dependent upon my parents.

Mum was always really sweet and loving and encouraging. But it was to Dad that I always felt the closest. I knew that if Dad was there, everything would be all right. Dad would sort everything out. In my eyes, he could do absolutely nothing wrong. This was true even when his reactions frightened me. Although he could be such great fun, he has always been a powerful, strict and quite aggressive man.

Once, I was lying in bed when Dad discovered that I'd made marks on the wall by banging it with the metal knobs on the end of the string that opened the curtains. He went absolutely berserk and stormed into Sally's room. When he discovered she'd done the same thing, he grabbed the piggy banks we had just been given by Nanny and dropped them over the landing, smashing them.

But I never used to blame him for anything he did. It was always somebody else's fault – mine, Sally's, my mother's. Dad just touches something in me. It's difficult to explain, but my heart really goes out to him. Despite his arrogance, I have always felt so much love for him. I never wanted to see him upset. It would really hurt me if I saw him hurt. There is something about him that is so lovely. He seems so boyish and so naïve, so open and so vulnerable.

# CHAPTER TWO

## *The Witch's Dance*

When I was eleven, I passed the scholarship examination to enter the same girls' grammar school that Mum had attended for a few years, until her father had moved her to a technical school because he thought it was better for her to train to be a secretary than go on, as she secretly wished, to an art school.

I was rather unpopular with the other girls. They said I was stuck up because I'd been to a private school, lived in a big house, wore my hair in a pony-tail and carried a little sling purse. I suppose I was something of a prig and a goody-goody. My classmates were very different and I didn't have any empathy for people at that age.

I didn't look or feel in any way attractive. I was still wearing my glasses when I started at the grammar school but, shortly afterwards, Mum and Dad arranged for me to have contact lenses. This wasn't because I was a vain child. I really needed to have sharp vision when I was dancing. If I did a pirouette wearing glasses, they'd go flying; without them, everything was a blur.

I took dancing very seriously. I was very dedicated and a real perfectionist. Every morning I'd do my exercises and every evening I'd go to dancing classes. I was also in a show at the dancing school and was such a success that, to my great delight, my dancing teacher suggested I enter a competition at the next Sidcup Dance Festival. It was something I knew I was going to enjoy.

* * *

By this time, the Owen family's way of life was extremely
comfortable. Ed and Pam had finished with the hard
work of their twenties when they were looking after
three very young children. Ed's business was well established and Pam worked for him in the office they had
created at home. As the novelty of being married
had worn off, they started going out to parties, togged
up to the nines. Both Ed and Pam were very popular and
enjoyed the swinging party scene. At the time, it was
all great fun and they didn't feel the children were
neglected. They always had baby-sitters the children
liked. So they never made Ed and Pam feel guilty for
going out.

Because of his business, Ed was away from home quite
a lot. This led him to decide that, instead of working from
the office in the house with Pam as his part-time typist,
he needed to have his own separate office in Sidcup with
a full-time secretary. Pam readily agreed to this and helped
find both the new offices and the secretary but then,
suddenly, she felt as though she wasn't necessary to Ed
any more. Her confidence was further undermined when,
after Ed's first day at his new offices, she asked him how
the new secretary had been.

'She's just as good as you are!' he said, hoping
perhaps to reassure her that everything would be all
right.

Feeling rejected, Pam spiralled down into a deep
depression. Alone in the house, with her three children
at school and her husband working away from home,
she felt desolate and wanted to do nothing but weep.

It was then that a male acquaintance asked her out to
lunch. Soon they were having an affair. Pam wasn't very
happy in this anomalous situation because she still loved
her husband and knew that, if questioned, she would be
incapable of telling lies.

26

Eventually, one Monday evening in December, three months after Nicola had started at grammar school, Ed confronted his wife. She confessed all and there was the most traumatic scene. Eventually, they went to bed exhausted but they still argued until two in the morning. The next day, the row continued. It went on all week.

On the Friday evening, Nicola came home from school to say she'd hurt her back when she'd fallen off a stool in the science laboratory. As she hadn't been brought home but had come on the bus as normal, Ed and Pam didn't make a lot of it. The next morning, they were lying miserable and silent in bed when Nicola came into the bedroom and asked if she could take Sally and Johnnie to do some Christmas shopping in Sidcup High Street.

Ed and Pam gladly agreed and gave the three children some pocket money. An hour or so later, there was a knock at the door. When Ed opened it, he found Nicola standing there crying.

Pale and shaking, she gasped, 'I can't breathe. My back's hurting dreadfully!'

Ed and Pam were distraught. Nicola was rushed to hospital where it was discovered that she had bronchial pneumonia and a collapsed lung. She was immediately taken into intensive care and put in an oxygen tent. The medical staff became very concerned that Nicola wasn't responding to antibiotics, presumably because she'd been given so many before to deal with her bronchial asthma, her sore throats and her severed tendons. The doctor advised Ed that he and Pam could visit Nicola at any time for as long as they wished.

Both Ed and Pam blamed themselves for what had happened. They felt they'd been so involved in their long-running row that they'd taken inadequate notice of what Nicola had told them about her accident.

Pam was convinced that it was her personal punishment.

Although things were still not right between the two of them, they were both so worried about Nicola that they stopped rowing. After a period when they'd been gradually drifting apart, Nicola's severe illness brought Pam and Ed firmly back together again.

Slowly, Nicola recovered. As soon as the oxygen tent had been taken away, she said, 'Don't have my name removed from the entrants' list of the Sidcup Festival. I shall be dancing there. You wait and see.'

Ed and Pam smiled in agreement, fully aware that, short of a miracle, there was no possibility of Nicola taking part in the festival. It was only six weeks away. But as soon as she could after leaving hospital, Nicola started to practise rigorously, displaying her characteristic iron will and determination.

\* \* \*

I had been entered for only one category in the Sidcup Festival – the character dance. I was to be 'Little Betty Blue'. Mrs Sutton, my teacher, told Mum what the costume should be like. Mum was excited and spent hours cutting it out and sewing it. The dress she made was beautiful with a very delicate-patterned material around the bottom. But when Mrs Sutton saw it she said, 'What a pity you didn't put that material on the top as well!' So Mum unpicked the whole costume and remade it, adding the patterned material on the top.

Full of confidence, I went to the festival and won my dance competition. After this, my dancing teacher started to take much more interest in me. In the next festival, I did two dances and then I gradually built up so that I was entering all the classes – tap, ballet, modern, character and national dancing. I didn't win every competition, but I won most of them and I was always placed.

My parents did everything they could to encourage me. They were the kind of people who, if they saw their child had a talent, felt that their child should have the best. I had everything I wanted. We bought things from the most exclusive ballet shops. I was taken to see the Bolshoi and the Royal Ballet. Mum spent hours getting my costumes right and taking me to dancing lessons. Dad was incredibly proud and recognized that I had real talent. They both did and were really excited by it. Other people might have thought my parents were being pushy but, even if they were, they were pushing me where I wanted to go, because I would have done it anyway.

Performing was something I'd been brought up with, because I lived in a very theatrical home. Both my parents were great exhibitionists by nature. Although by profession Dad was a chartered accountant, he loved playing the piano at parties and dressing up to entertain us all. One Christmas Day, he put on some pink dancing tights and pushed a cricket box and four pairs of rolled up socks over his crutch. Then he and Nanny, who was dressed as the Sugar Plum Fairy, did their own hilarious version of 'The Nutcracker Suite'. Mum was just as bad. Once, I was having breakfast with Sally and Johnnie before going off to school, when Mum slid down the banisters in her red negligé, jumped on the kitchen table and started singing, 'Hey, Big Spender'. So ours was the kind of household where, if you didn't make a show, you weren't noticed.

It was impossible for me to compete with my parents at home, but I could perform on the stage and I loved it. I loved the atmosphere, the make-up, the lights and the applause. While I was waiting for my turn, I'd feel the adrenalin speeding through me and I'd be so nervous – astonishingly nervous. But as soon as I was in front of an audience, I felt truly alive. I knew that I was good and that I had something special to offer the people who were watching. I had no doubts that it was what I was meant to do in life. In time, dancing teachers, everybody, said that I had outstanding talent and genuine star quality; that I was destined to go to the top. I never doubted this for a moment. I was delighted that I had the talent and had been able to develop it. It made me feel very special. I shall never ever feel as happy as I did then. They were magical times.

Yet I was also aware that I had two personalities. There was the complete confidence and maturity I felt onstage when I was a real entertainer and very professional. But offstage I was back to being a well-behaved, somewhat introverted schoolgirl.

At school, I still wasn't accepted by my classmates. It didn't help that there was often something in the local newspapers about my winning medals and cups at various dancing festivals. Also I was still very skinny and flat-chested when all the other girls in my class seemed to have developed breasts and were wearing bras. So Mum bought me one with an A-cup size. It was absurd really. The bra was quite unnecessary, but I felt better wearing one like the other girls.

Seeing that I wasn't very happy at school, Mum said, 'For your thirteenth birthday, we'll have a tramps' supper party and you can invite all the girls in your class.' It was a spectacular success. Dad erected a huge tent in the garden. He invented different games which were set up around the lawn. And Mum organized fantastic food and a barbecue. Everybody came dressed as tramps and had a great time. They thought Dad was terrific and several girls said he looked like Paul Newman. After that, I was extremely popular with the girls in my class – so much so that I was elected form captain three times in a row.

*   *   *

Shortly after Nicola's thirteenth birthday, she was due to compete in an important dance festival. As always, her parents did what they could to help and support her. It had become part of the ritual preparation for a festival that Nicola would rehearse her new dances in the lounge. A large central area was cleared by pushing the sofa and armchairs into the corners of the room and heaping on to them the coffee tables and lamps. It was Sally's job to operate the cassette-recorder used to play the music for the dance.

One of the new dances Nicola was preparing for the festival was a portrayal of Carmen. In the lounge, Ed intently watched the routine of his slender, thirteen-year-old daughter.

Interrupting her dance, he announced in an animated staccato, 'No, no, Nicola. You're Carmen. Spanish blood and all that! Brittle sensitivity! Quick to love and to hate! You're supposed to be a temptress of men. You've got to feel that hot, passionate blood coursing through your veins. Your whole body's that of a gypsy. You have loved and now you are hating. You are jealous and you are thinking of revenge.'

Catching her mother's eye, Nicola smiled coyly and asked innocently, 'What would you suggest, Dad?'

Off came Ed's shoes, his trousers were rolled half-way up his legs and in the centre of the floor he struck the pose of what he felt sure was a typical Spanish dancer. 'Turn it on, Sally,' he commanded. 'Come on, Sally. More volume.' The music blared out. 'Right, let's go,' he said and with his stomach taut and bottom protruding he gyrated across the floor in what he took to be a co-ordinated series of jetés and pirouettes. His arms were thrust out in all directions as he made exaggerated gestures with his hands and fingers.

Pam was curled on the sofa, trying desperately to stifle her laughter. She was firmly holding her sides and her eyes were brimming with tears. Sally, who had been sitting on the floor beside the cassette-recorder, made no such attempt to keep quiet. She was lying flat on her back, her whole body shaking with laughter.

Finding breath at last, Pam called out between peals of laughter, 'Stop, Ed, for goodness' sake. You're killing us!'

Panting from his exertions, Ed turned to Nicola, who had collapsed into one of the laden armchairs in near hysterics. 'Got the idea now, Nicola?' he asked.

His question was greeted with gales of laughter from his wife and two daughters.

\* \* \*

One evening, some six weeks after my thirteenth birthday, I was sitting in my green dressing-gown at the desk in my bedroom. Mum was getting ready for bed. Suddenly, I felt something sticky between my thighs. I opened my dressing-gown and saw there was blood on my night-dress. It took me totally by surprise. I rushed in to Mum and said, 'Oh, Mum, look!' Then, I don't know why, I started to cry.

Mum put her arms round me and said, 'It's all right, Nicola. You've started your first period. I was just like that when I started mine. Come on. Let's sort you out.'

She told me what I had to do and showed me how to use a sanitary towel. Yet, for years afterwards, I had a big hang-up about going into a chemist and asking for sanitary towels. So Mum used to buy them for me and I wondered if I'd ever be confident enough to buy them myself. I used to think that, if I left home, I'd just have to make do with wads of toilet paper. It was all so embarrassing.

The day after I started my first period was the important dancing festival. That night, as I lay in bed, I felt quite a martyr – the following day I'd be dancing while I was bleeding.

\* \* \*

On the morning of the festival, Ed, as always, rose early, awakened by the electric alarm clock deliberately placed on a chest of drawers remote from the comfortable warmth of the bed. It was Saturday and so all the family would be going along to see Nicola dance.

After laying a tray with cups of tea, Ed returned to the bedroom and woke his wife by kissing her gently on the neck. Sleepily sipping her warm tea, she mentally checked off the collection of dance costumes arrayed around the room in their protective plastic covers. With her dedicated perfectionism, she had, as always, ensured that everything was ready for the festival – the peach ballet dress, the tap-dance costume with royal blue top and trousers covered with hundreds of sequins she'd sewn on by hand, the exotic Hungarian national costume and the new dress she had made from grey and black chiffon for 'The Witch from Hansel and Gretel'. On the dressing-table stood its accompanying tall, black, shiny hat, grey ragged wig, black shawl and long, green finger-nails.

Nicola was already awake. She was soon in her parents' bedroom, bubbling with excitement. 'Come on, Mum,' she demanded. 'There's a lot to be done.'

Pam smiled and patiently said, 'All right, Nicola, I'm on my way.' Soon, under Nicola's ever-watchful eye, she was collecting all the costumes together.

Sally was usually far more difficult to rouse than her sister. Ed went through his ritual of opening her door, putting on her bedside cabinet a cup of tea that would normally remain untouched and waking her with a weather report: 'Morning, Sally. The day looks fine and there's a soft wind coming from the south-west.'

Aware that it was the day of the festival, Sally didn't need a second call. 'Thanks, Dad,' she said and sat up with a quick shake of her curly, dark-brown hair. She really enjoyed going to watch Nicola dance at the festivals. She loved the glamour of the costumes, the make-up and the music. Not so long ago, she had been very much the

33

centre of attention within the family but now, because Nicola had become such a talented dancer, it was her sister's successes that seemed to be her parents' main topic of conversation. She might well have been jealous of Nicola, but she wasn't. Sally admired her elder sister and felt proud of her achievements.

When Ed entered his son's room, Johnnie was fast asleep, his head and body totally hidden beneath the orange bed-cover. Ed gently shook what he took to be a shoulder. Johnnie, a charming and good-natured young boy, immediately pulled back the covers and grinned at his father. He too knew that it was the day of the festival. He was only eight and he would go along with his parents without complaint, keeping his thoughts about it to himself. Unlike Sally, he found it impossible not to be jealous of Nicola. He felt resentful that she seemed to be given all the attention. She was the great dancer and he had no interest in dancing. He hated going to the festivals. He would have much preferred being left in the house with his friends. The last thing he wanted to do was to stand around with a load of mums, watching girls prance around the stage.

After everybody had eaten breakfast and the dresses had been stacked in the car, the Owen family set off for the large hall where the festival was to be held. There they joined the mêlée of young girls and their parents who, laden with armfuls of skimpy costumes and make-up boxes, were struggling through the open swing doors. Very conscious that he had parked illegally, Ed was in a hurry, but he still had time to notice that, despite the all-pervading smell of polish, there was, regrettably, a thin coating of dust in the hall.

When the car had been unloaded, Ed drove off, looking for a safe place to park. Nicola went to the dressing-room with Pam who would be spending much of the day helping her with her costumes and make-up. Sally and Johnnie gravitated towards the refreshment bar to join the excited

34

babble of slim young dancers who seemed able to consume innumerable bars of chocolate and bags of crisps, washing them down with astonishing amounts of squash and mineral water.

As the festival competition was classified not only by dance style but also by age groups, there was a constant succession of adjudications and medal presentations. The repetition inevitably deflated the initial bubble of excitement and the audience thinned out as parents left for refreshments or to attend to their children, praising the victors and consoling the losers. Only when a particularly talented dancer was about to perform did the number of people in the auditorium significantly increase. This happened each time Nicola was due to dance. And she clearly was outstanding. With one dance left to perform, she had already been awarded five firsts. The final category was the Character Dance.

The auditorium was crowded for Nicola's performance. As for all the other dances, the stage was brilliantly lit. Pam hurried back from the dressing-room and reclaimed her seat next to Ed. Leaning over to Sally and Johnnie, she whispered, 'She looks fantastic.' The audience hushed expectantly.

The pianist struck up a heavy discordant rhythm that rapidly increased in volume. A hand slowly appeared, spreading its fingers with their long green nails as it grasped the curtain and pulled it gradually towards the side of the stage. As the crashing piano chords reverberated through the auditorium, a pointed black hat edged out from behind the curtain just above the clutching hand. A shoe and a black-stockinged foot appeared, tentatively poised as though searching for a safe place to stand on a frozen lake. As the music abruptly stopped and the face beneath the hat jerked into view, the audience gasped and young girls screamed. The penetrating eyes of the deathly white face were encircled with vivid green and the emerald lips were parted to reveal blackened, rotting teeth.

The music restarted and the slender figure in ragged black and grey spun out in grotesque whirls towards the centre of the stage. Arms reached out like the gnarled boughs of an ancient oak. Framed by matted grey hair, the face reappeared over a hunched shoulder. Again, young girls screamed in unison and some let out gasps of genuine horror. Every inch of the body, every movement of the arm and leg, every grotesque facial expression left no one in any doubt that this was a witch.

At the end, there was a stunned silence, eventually broken by a tentative hand clap which rapidly crescendoed into the thunderous applause that acknowledges an outstanding performance. Pam was flushed with excitement and pride. As Ed clapped along with all the others, he too shared these emotions, but there was something else that he felt deep down inside him – something so disturbing that his whole being told him that even the possibility of its existence should be denied. Yet being at once logical and emotional, he was incapable of ignoring what he felt.

It was her eyes – Nicola's eyes! He'd seen a glimpse of madness in her eyes as she performed the witch's dance and it was not a madness conjured up for a spectacular performance – it was real. Ed hated himself for even formulating the thought but, try as he would, he couldn't escape the deeply disturbing conviction that Nicola's eyes spoke the truth. He knew it was a fear he must not express. He was not to know how soon it would be before his fear became realized. Then, rather than being merely a character on stage producing screams of terror from young children in the audience, Nicola, grotesquely changed, would produce a wave of terror that would endanger his whole family.

In the dressing-room after Nicola's last triumphant dance, Pam helped her jubilant daughter remove her make-up and then her costume which was carefully put away in its plastic bag. Having gathered all the dresses together, Pam was waiting for Nicola to finish changing, when an acquaintance, who was the mother of another competitor, came up to her and congratulated her on Nicola's successes.

'Yes, Nicola's such a good little girl,' Pam replied pleasantly. 'She's like a little angel.'

'Don't ever say that!' the woman chillingly exclaimed. 'Something terrible might happen!'

\*    \*    \*

As soon as I stepped on stage, something suddenly changed within me. I was no longer a little girl performing, I was a grown woman and I knew that I'd wipe the floor with all the competition at the festival.

I danced for the pleasure of dancing, using my body for the movement, for the way I felt. When I was Carmen, I was the jealous lover. When I was doing an Indian dance, I was an Apache brave. With the witch dance, I was the witch and I became so carried away that, when I was supposed to be pushed into an oven by Hansel and Gretel, I actually screamed out. It wasn't intended, but I'd become so involved in the role. I'd never danced so well.

I won all six of the categories I'd entered and I was also awarded the cup for the candidate who, in the adjudicator's opinion, would be most likely to succeed in the future. Sitting in the car on the way home, I was overwhelmed with a wonderful sense of optimism, thinking to myself, Oh, this is terrific! I've got this fabulous career ahead of me, I'm maturing into a woman and I've got all this talent. Isn't life amazing? Everything's so exciting.

# CHAPTER THREE

## *Family Break*

A week after the festival, the annual family holiday began. Mum had managed to persuade Dad that we should go to Majorca on our first package tour rather than embark on another camping holiday.

The previous summer's holiday had been an unprecedented disaster. After two days in the South of France, we'd been engulfed in an unending downpour and had to evacuate to Italy where, after three days, the rain caught up with us and we spent the next two days sitting in a wooden hut on the site playing Scrabble. As soon as the rain stopped, we headed for home. It was because Dad had an obsession with not returning with any foreign currency that the final farcical incident happened just a few miles away from the car ferry at Boulogne. The car ran out of petrol, Dad had to hitch-hike to the nearest garage, he had no francs left and the proprietor wouldn't accept sterling. Dad was forced to pay double the going exchange rate to a passing motorist so he could obtain the few francs' worth of petrol we needed to get us to the ferry.

After dinner on the third day of our holiday in Majorca, Mum and Dad retired to the hotel bar with an English couple they'd met. I went off with Sally, Johnnie and two friends – a boy of my age and his sister. They wanted to show us their room and so we took the lift up to the second floor. When we reached it, we turned left and walked along the corridor. At the end there was a right-angled turn and at that point I suddenly slipped on the tiled floor and fell badly.

I knew immediately that I'd broken my left leg which was bent beneath the right one. It was very painful, but I didn't scream or even cry. All I wanted to do was to stand up and let my leg dangle. I tried to get up, but the boy held me down and Sally ran off to fetch Dad.

He must have flown up the stairs, because in no time at all he was running down the corridor towards me. 'I'm here, Nick,' he said. 'Mum's just on her way.'

I lay perfectly still and said, 'I'm ever so sorry, Dad. I think I've broken my leg.'

Dad immediately knelt down and inspected my leg. As he'd played a lot of football, he'd seen many broken bones and so he instantly identified the slight indentation, the puckered skin and split veins at the bottom of my left shin. 'Don't worry,' he said, 'but I think you have broken it.' He then turned me slowly so that I could move my right leg and stretch out.

As the manoeuvre was taking place, I saw Mum rushing down the corridor with the English couple, who'd brought along a sour-faced woman and a middle-aged Spaniard with a moustache and a wobbling stomach that bulged over the thick leather belt which held up his creased white trousers.

'Don't worry, Mum,' I said. 'I'll be all right.'

Mum looked desperately at Dad and said, 'What's she done?'

Business-like as usual, Dad said, 'She's broken her shin all right. You can see it there. And I think she's done something pretty serious to her ankle as well.'

Mum cried out, 'Oh, no,' and fainted, hitting her head on the floor.

The sour-looking woman went to help her. The man with the moustache then said, 'I'm a doctor. We were in the bar when your friends came up and told us what had happened. That's my nurse,' he said, pointing to the woman who was by now helping Mum to her feet. 'She's from Belgium.'

'I speak English too,' the mousy-haired nurse said to Dad. 'Your wife's all right now. The English always make such a fuss.'

The doctor opened the door to one of the bedrooms and said, 'We can use this room here. Let's get your daughter on to the bed.'

Several people lifted me up, carried me into the room and laid me on the bed. The doctor lit up a giant cigar and announced that he would set my leg there and then. Dad was having none of it and said that I had to be taken immediately to a hospital so that my leg could be X-rayed to see if an operation was necessary.

As the hospital was in Palma, on the opposite side of the island, the doctor suggested taking a taxi rather than having to wait for an ambulance. Dad insisted on carrying me down to the taxi and I hung on to him while Mum supported my left foot. The journey was a nightmare, taking over an hour. Most of the time, Dad was crouched uncomfortably on the floor, cradling my broken leg. He kept on telling me to be brave. The pain was excruciating, but I didn't cry.

We were met at the hospital by the surgeon and I was wheeled in on a stretcher. My leg was then X-rayed and the following day it was operated on and encased in an enormous plaster – reaching from my hip to my toes – which was suspended on a hoist above the bed.

Dad and I shared a suite on the first floor. It was unbearably hot and I was very uncomfortable, lying there with little or nothing to do. Dad was always rushing off to buy me special treats. It must have been terribly boring for him, but I didn't think about it. It just seemed right that it was Dad who was always there.

On the fifth day, for no apparent reason, I was suddenly hit with a blinding headache and felt really low. Dad seemed to think that all I needed was to be cheered up but when his attempts to jolly me along failed, he started on a different tack, saying that I wasn't the only one suffering and that what had happened was spoiling everybody's holiday. I threw a tantrum. It wasn't my fault I'd broken my leg and I didn't want to be lying in a stinking hot hospital. So why didn't he get off my back and leave me alone?

Dad's patience snapped and he slapped my face. I immediately went rigid and he rushed out of the room. A little while later, he returned, took me in his arms, kissed me on the forehead and tearfully said, 'Forgive me, Nicola. I just don't know what got into me.'

'There's nothing to forgive, Dad,' I said truthfully. 'It was all my fault.' I was deeply moved. I didn't need to be hugged or kissed or anything like that to know he loved me. He didn't have to say a word. There was a special bond between us and it didn't need anything more. I just knew what Dad felt for me and I knew what I felt for Dad.

After a week in the hospital, I was taken back to the hotel. Still swathed in plaster, I spent most of the daytime on a sunbed under the shade of a large fir tree, close to the hotel swimming pool. Because I was something of a celebrity, I always seemed to be surrounded by young people, all of whom wanted to sign their names on my plaster.

I spent the nights on a camp-bed on the balcony outside my bedroom. One morning, I swung my broken leg out of the bed and it just dropped. I knew immediately I'd done something wrong, but I didn't say anything about it to anyone.

When we returned home, I was taken to see the surgeon who'd operated on my hand when I'd accidentally cut through the tendons and cartilage. He said my leg would have to be reset and there was a chance that it might end up being a little shorter than my right leg.

I was stunned but Mum refused to accept this possibility. 'Oh, no, doctor,' she said determinedly. 'Nicola wants to be a dancer. We can't have this. Surely something can be done.'

'Well, Mrs Owen,' he replied calmly. 'I can't guarantee that this will succeed, but it will help considerably if

Nicola can be kept in bed for three weeks with her leg up at about thirty degrees from the mattress. It's also essential that during that time she doesn't get up at all.'

And so that's what was done. I spent the next three weeks lain out in a bed that had been brought down into the sitting-room. So that I wouldn't need to get up, I was given a large bed pan. To ensure my leg was constantly elevated at the prescribed angle, my mother watched over me like a hawk, even to the extent of getting up in the middle of the night. As I lay there, hour after hour, I became ever more determined to dance again.

When the three weeks of inactivity were over, the doctor assured Mum and I that the leg had set well. I was given crutches and told that I couldn't put any weight on my leg for another twelve weeks. With my leg fully encased in plaster, I went along to my dance classes. Even if I wasn't able to join in, at least I could watch and take in everything that was happening.

Dad was so impressed by my determination to continue with my dancing that he decided to build a dance studio for me in part of the garage. He and Mum's father partitioned it off, put in a door, painted all the walls and put red linoleum on the floor. Grandad managed to get hold of a huge mirror that he fixed firmly to the wall. Dad bought a long oval rail which was mounted on brass brackets to run as a barre across the mirror. Mum put up some dancing pictures and fitted pretty floral curtains at the window. As a finishing touch, Nanny bought me a plaque to put on the door – 'Nicola's Dance Studio'.

I was thrilled and it made me even more determined. Even though my leg was still in plaster and I had to walk with the aid of crutches, I started to get up at six o'clock every morning and go down to my studio. I'd stand on my right leg and swing the one in plaster, practise my arm exercises and limber up the rest of my body. Even Mrs Sutton, my dancing teacher, freaked out when she visited me and saw me at the barre swinging up my leg, totally encased in plaster.

When the full-length plaster was replaced by one that ended just below the knee, the nurse at the hospital told me that I should go to a physiotherapist three times a week. Knowing that this meant it was going to be a long-drawn-out process, I refused. My knee had become set and stiff. So I spent the day in Dad's office, sitting in his chair and forcing my leg to move up and down. By the end of the day, I was able to bend my knee.

Wearing the much lighter leg plaster meant that I could go back to school, but I was desperate to resume my dancing classes. Mrs Sutton agreed that I could do so after the doctor had said I was able to put weight on my left leg again. But I couldn't wait. Each evening there was a class, I put on a leotard and one ballet shoe, Mum drove me to the school and, with half my leg still in plaster, I joined in. Mrs Sutton was so impressed with me that, after Christmas, she invited me to help teach the little children on Saturday mornings. I was thrilled to be asked.

The leg plaster was finally removed at the end of February. At that time, the dancing school was preparing for a public display in April. When I said that I wanted to take part, Mrs Sutton said, 'But you'll have been out of plaster for only six weeks.' I insisted that I would be ready and, although I wasn't given any big solos, I was allowed to take part.

To my astonishment, this decision seemed to cause a lot of resentment from other girls attending the dancing school. There was so much competitiveness among us all and perhaps they'd assumed that, after my accident, I would no longer be a threat at the dancing festivals. Whatever the reason, as the display came closer, the atmosphere became even more strained.

On the first night, I fell over on stage although I got up immediately and finished the dance. When I returned to the dressing-room, the other girls were laughing at me and one of them snapped, 'We've all been working hard for months for this. You've let us down, Nicola. You've been back on your feet for only a couple of weeks. You shouldn't have been in the display.'

It was the first time I'd ever experienced bitchiness and it unnerved me a little. It also made me even more determined to do well. On the following evenings, I gave flawless performances. A few weeks later, I entered every competition at a festival and won them all, apart from ballet which was on points, but I came second in that.

I suppose, being so successful, I was somewhat full of myself. Perhaps because of this I started getting impatient with my mother. When she was fitting me for my costumes, I knew it was for my benefit, but it always seemed to take an age and I quickly became irritable. When we went to dance festivals, I began to be off-hand with her, but not deliberately. I didn't consciously feel any animosity to her at that stage.

As I knew that I wanted to be a professional dancer, I realized I would have to move from my dancing school to a more senior one. I'd been very happy at my old school, but the unpleasantness I'd experienced during the April display made it easier for me to leave.

So, in the autumn, I started attending dancing lessons at the Doreen Bird School of Acting and Dance in Sidcup. She was an excellent teacher, but there was one drawback that at first I didn't think would be of any great importance. Doreen Bird wouldn't allow any of her students to enter competitive dance festivals. As a result, just after my fourteenth birthday, I stopped doing the thing that during the previous four years had brought me the greatest excitement and pleasure I'd ever experienced.

At this time, I was maturing into a young woman. I had blossomed from an ugly duckling, skinny and bespectacled, into a beautiful young woman. My skin was perfect and, because of all the exercise I did, I had a firm body and impressive figure.

Initially, I paid no attention to my looks. I think that, at first, Sally was more aware of them than I was. She had always been interested in boys and she was going through a stage when she was terribly self-conscious about the way she looked. She had very bad acne and was quite dumpy. I think it really upset her that, when we went to the park, boys would tell me how pretty I was and people would stare at me as I walked down the street.

Soon I really enjoyed being stared at and creating an impact wherever I went. Until then, I'd only really been an object of attention when I was on stage. Now I had local photographers stopping me in the street to ask if I would model for them. I suppose it began to go to my head. I became full of my own self-importance, feeling that I was superior to other people because of the way I looked.

Perhaps because I was no longer performing in front of audiences at dancing festivals, I became something of an exhibitionist, especially at school. I'd have little scenes in the classroom when I'd pretend to lose my contact lenses and get the teachers to grovel on the floor to look for them. I ran the school gambling syndicate where pontoon was played for ten pence, which was considered to be serious money. One morning, I used make-up to black out the teeth of everybody in the class so when the headmistress walked in and we all said, 'Good morning, Miss Mason,' she nearly had a heart attack. My school work began to suffer and if a teacher wrote a comment in an exercise book I'd write one in reply. Not surprisingly, I started getting into a lot of trouble.

My mother and sister both had problems with their weight, but I didn't. I was very skinny and could eat what I liked without putting on weight. They always seemed to be going on a diet that everybody else had to follow, when sweets, biscuits and puddings tended to disappear.

I assumed that it was because of this that I suddenly got the desire to eat enormous quantities. At school, in front of everybody, I'd eat twelve packets of crisps or a pound's worth of sweets. I didn't think that it was strange, but there were times when I just ate and ate.

It seemed as if it was something I couldn't control. At the same time, I was worried that I might start putting on weight. Now that I had a woman's body, I was no longer a skinny wraith. So I got into the habit of making myself sick after an eating binge. I'd read somewhere that you could do this by drinking salt water. When there was no one around at home, I'd put a couple of inches of salt in the bottom of a pint pewter tankard and pour in warm water to dissolve the salt. Then I'd take a deep breath and drink it down. As I did so, I'd go hot all over. It would be about half an hour before it took effect and all the time I'd feel nauseous. Then I'd be sick and feel terribly cold.

I wasn't upset by it. It seemed a sensible thing to do. And why should I be upset? My life was so rosy. A fantastic career as a dancer stretched ahead of me. I had a beautiful home and loving parents who encouraged me all the way. Because I had a pretty face and a good figure, I was doing photographic modelling. Girls at school would say, 'It's so unfair, Nicola. You've got everything. You've been handed it all on a plate and you really don't appreciate it.' And I suppose I did take it all for granted. The world, I felt sure, was my oyster. How could anything possibly go wrong?

# CHAPTER FOUR

## *Overdose*

One Saturday night in January, when I was fourteen and a half, my parents went to visit some friends in Beckenham. For the first time, I'd been left to baby-sit for Sally and Johnnie. After they'd gone to bed, I sat crossed-legged on the floor, watching an old Elvis Presley movie. It was really sweet and slushy but, suddenly, for no apparent reason, I felt unbearably miserable and started to cry. I switched off the television and stared at the blank screen for ages and ages.

I couldn't understand what was happening because I'd never had such feelings before. It was just as though I had been swimming along happily beneath a clear blue sky when, out of nowhere, a gigantic tidal wave suddenly immersed me in a sea of unbearable misery. Everything about me seemed black and lifeless. I had no energy to fight against it. All I could do was weep.

Trying to work out why I felt as I did, I recalled that, a week earlier, I'd seen a programme on television about a lovely young girl who'd tried to commit suicide. She'd been rushed into hospital where all the young doctors fell in love with her and saved her life. Suddenly, I felt sure that there was something seriously wrong with me and I too needed help.

Still crying, I walked into the kitchen, not knowing what I was going to do. I opened the larder door and, for a brief moment, I thought of eating as much as I could but,

47

instead, I reached up to the top shelf and took down the only two bottles of pills that were there – the antibiotics I took when I had bronchial asthma and some iron tablets my father had bought in the hope they'd give him more stamina when playing squash.

I shook both lots of tablets into my hand and put back the two bottles. Then I poured myself a glass of water and, without having an idea what the effect might be, I swallowed my handful of tablets. Even as I took them, I didn't know why I was doing it. I was so totally mixed up and overwhelmed by a deep black depression.

Crying all the time, I went upstairs to my room, undressed, slipped on my night-dress, climbed into bed and switched off the light. What have I done? I thought. Perhaps I'm going to die. Even though I felt exhausted, I couldn't stop crying and it was an age before I managed to fall asleep.

At about two in the morning, I woke up in a panic. Bursting into tears, I jumped out of bed and put on my dressing-gown and slippers. Not bothering to see if Mum and Dad had returned, I went downstairs and left the house. I'd no real idea of what I was going to do but, with tears streaming down my face, I set off walking towards Sidcup – some three miles away. Fortunately, although it was the middle of January, it was a mild night. But, because there was no moon, it was very, very dark. The occasional glare of a passing car's headlights and the seemingly tortured screams of night birds made me walk faster and faster. Wherever I was going, I knew I had to get there as quickly as possible.

Arriving in Sidcup, I walked into the police station. I could see that the two policemen on duty thought I was some kind of lunatic from the way they looked at me – crying hysterically and wearing a dressing-gown and slippers. 'You've got to help me,' I sobbed. 'I've taken some tablets . . . In fact, I've taken a lot of tablets.'

I was desperately unhappy but, for a fleeting moment,

it felt just as though I was in a play, although I didn't have the slightest idea of why I was acting as I was.

\* \* \*

At first, Ed thought it was the alarm clock but, as he came out of his deep sleep, he realized that the sound was the insistent ringing of the bedside telephone. After a momentary grope in the darkness, he picked it up.

'Ed Owen,' he said.

'Mr Owen?'

'That's what I said.'

'This is Sidcup Police Station. We have your daughter, Nicola, here.'

'Get lost,' Ed barked impatiently and banged down the phone.

'Who was that?' Pam asked sleepily.

'Some crank. Turn over and let's get back to sleep.'

The phone rang again. 'Who is that?' Ed demanded.

'Mr Owen, this is Sergeant Williams at Sidcup Police Station. We have your daughter, Nicola, here.'

Still not properly awake, Ed couldn't understand the situation. When he and Pam had returned from Beckenham, they'd carefully checked their children's bedrooms and Johnnie, Sally and Nicola were safely tucked up in bed, fast asleep. Ed tried desperately to focus his eyes on the distant alarm clock. 'What time is it?' he asked.

'It's just after two forty-five, Mr Owen.'

Ed suddenly became annoyed. 'I don't know who the hell you are,' he snapped, 'but my daughter, Nicola, is in bed.'

Hearing this, Pam jumped out of bed and ran to Nicola's bedroom. She quickly returned, saying, 'She's not there, Ed.'

Ed caught the fear in her voice. 'My wife say's she's

not in her room,' he said. 'Hang on, sergeant. I'll search the rest of the house.'

He shot out of bed, told Pam to check the other children's rooms and ran downstairs to look for Nicola. As he came back up the stairs, Pam was standing at the top, anxiously shaking her head. There was no sign of Nicola anywhere in the house.

Ed again picked up the phone. 'Sergeant Williams, she's not here. I don't understand how she's got to you.'

'She says she's walked the whole way. She's only wearing a night-dress and dressing-gown. She claims she's swallowed a lot of pills.'

'Pills, did you say? What pills?'

'We don't know, sir, but we're taking her to hospital. Perhaps you could bring along with you any bottles of pills you've got in the house. I shouldn't delay, sir. I'll phone the hospital to tell them you'll be bringing them.'

'Thank you, sergeant. We're on our way.'

Pam was already nearly dressed. Ed told her to wake up Sally and Johnnie while he checked the bathroom cabinet and larder for bottles of pills. He found only the antibiotics and the iron tablets. Back in his bedroom, to save as much time as possible, he pulled on his trousers and a sweater over his pyjamas and put on his slippers.

With their two younger children, who were still half asleep, Ed and Pam tumbled into the car in a turmoil, terrified that Nicola might be going to die. Five minutes after Sergeant Williams' telephone call, they were on the way to the hospital.

As Ed stared intently at the road ahead, his mind harked back to something that had happened a couple of months earlier. When he and Pam returned home from an evening out, the regular baby-sitter reported that, as she and the three children had been together in the sitting-room, they had heard a strange bump somewhere upstairs. At first, everybody was scared, thinking there must be somebody in one of the bedrooms, but

50

when the baby-sitter went to investigate, she discovered with some relief the cause of the unexpected sound. A framed picture was lying face down on the landing. The only strange thing was that she could find no reason why it should be there – the hanging wire was unbroken and the picture hook was still firmly fixed in the wall. In itself, the incident might have been of no great importance if it hadn't been that Ed recalled only too well his mother's firmly-held conviction that, if a painting or photograph fell off the wall, it was a terrible omen. Ed had been somewhat alarmed, therefore, to discover that the painting that had so mysteriously slipped from the landing wall was a print of Degas' 'La Classe', showing, as it did, a group of young ballet dancers patiently listening to their tutor.

When the Owens arrived at the casualty department of the hospital, the receptionist seemed to be expecting them and asked them to wait for a few moments. Full of foreboding and trying hard not to further alarm their two sleepy children, Ed and Pam sat down uneasily on the cheap-looking chairs in the almost deserted reception area.

After a couple of minutes, a staff nurse arrived and Ed handed over the two bottles of pills he had found. She studied the labels carefully and said, 'They seem to correspond to what Nicola has told us. The tablets aren't going to do her any harm, but we've stomach-pumped her just to be on the safe side.'

Ed's and Pam's relief was tangible. Ed even managed to smile weakly at the nurse as she handed him back the empty bottles.

Looking quizzically at Pam, the nurse asked, 'Have you any idea what made your daughter do this, Mrs Owen?'

Pam shook her head. 'No, we don't understand why on earth she did it,' she replied. 'Please can we see her now? We'd like to talk to her.'

'Yes, of course. I'll just have to check that the doctor

is all through. I think he would like to have a word with you both.'

When she returned, she escorted Ed and Pam into a ward where all the beds appeared to be enclosed by plastic curtains. She pulled one of them aside. Nicola was lying in bed talking to a white-coated doctor who looked up at them as they entered.

After they'd been quickly introduced, he said, 'I think we shall keep Nicola in for a few days. I'm going to recommend that she's seen by another doctor. I'm sure you would like to have a few minutes with Nicola before we settle her down for what remains of the night.'

Nicola looked up at her parents. It was the first time she'd ever seen real worry and concern in her father's eyes. He wasn't crying, but he was choking back the tears.

It was Pam who spoke first. 'Why have you done this, Nicola?' she said gently. 'Please tell us. We just don't understand. If you tell us, we can help you.'

'I don't know, Mum,' Nicola replied, beginning to cry. 'I honestly don't know why I did it.'

Deeply upset, but desperate to get to the bottom of it all, Ed blurted out, 'This is absolutely ridiculous, Nicola. It's crazy. Just tell me why, Nicola, why? What's it all about?'

'I don't know, Dad,' Nicola sobbed. 'I'm so sorry.'

Unable to understand, Ed was angry and perplexed. He needed a few minutes to sort out his confused emotions. 'I'm going to fetch Johnnie and Sally to see you,' he said and hurriedly left Nicola's bedside. It was the only positive action he felt he could take.

Seeing that Ed's sudden departure seemed to have further upset Nicola, Pam stood in silence gazing at her daughter's tear-stained but beautiful young face. She was deeply worried. Nicola had always been such a good girl, but she'd changed and although Pam couldn't put her finger on it, she was sure things weren't right. It must be similar, she reflected, to when a woman senses that her husband is having an affair. She can't actually prove anything, she can't explain why she feels as she does, but she's certain that she's right.

Recently, Nicola had been increasingly moody and Pam had begun to feel criticized by her, not directly but by her attitude. Much of the time, Pam wondered if she was to blame. Ed seemed to notice none of this. He was away from home a lot and Nicola was always very affectionate to him when he returned.

Ed was calmer when he came back with Sally and Johnnie. It was obvious there was nothing more they could do for Nicola that night and so, after a few minutes of desultory conversation, they all kissed her and, exhausted and bemused, drove silently back home.

Nicola was kept in hospital for three days. The doctor didn't consider that her overdose of pills was necessarily serious, but it was unusual that she had walked over three miles to a police station in the middle of the night. This, he felt, might be evidence that she was very disturbed. So Nicola was seen in hospital by 'another doctor' – Dr Goble, a consultant psychiatrist, who arranged for her to attend his clinic as an outpatient.

\*　　\*　　\*

I didn't relate to Dr Goble at all, although he was a very kindly man with a soft voice and gentle manner. We had long-drawn-out conversations about my past, my medical history and my dreams.

I told him I often dreamt that I couldn't escape from people who were chasing me. Often it was Apache braves. There were masses of places to hide and plenty of time, but my legs were leaden and I couldn't run. I'd keep on looking around, knowing in the end they were going to catch me. So, I'd stop and turn round to face them. It was just at that moment when they were about to kill me that I was most terrified. But I didn't wake up at that point. In my dream, they always killed me.

After a few weeks, Dr Goble suggested that instead of attending his clinic I should become a private patient and see him at his house. My parents agreed to this and on Monday evenings I'd be taken from my dancing classes to his home. Each time I went, I couldn't wait to leave because I thought it was a complete waste of time. I didn't think I was mad or unbalanced. There had just been one weird incident. I couldn't explain it, but I felt sure I wouldn't do it again.

I was much more worried that I was eating such a lot and had started to put on a little weight. I was five feet three inches tall and weighed seven stone eleven pounds. That was already more than I should have been as a fourteen-year-old dancer. I frequently discussed this with Dr Goble but, as he only saw a slim girl complaining about her weight, he concluded that I was potentially anorexic. Even though I told him that I veered between periods of starvation and bouts of compulsive overeating when, if necessary, I'd steal money from Mum's purse to buy food, he had no help to give.

He seemed to think that I was mainly suffering from nervous exhaustion and said he wanted to put some recommendations to my parents.

\*     \*     \*

Ed and Pam sat facing Dr Goble in what served as his consulting room – a cramped area curtained off from the rest of the lounge.

'I think that Nicola's commitments are too heavy,' he announced, peering at them through his gold-rimmed spectacles with their thick lenses that magnified his dark brown eyes enormously. 'I think this is putting undue pressure on her. After all, she's doing nine O level subjects at school and, apart from three dancing classes each week, she tells me that most mornings she's up by six o'clock to practise in her dance studio at home.'

'Yes, that's true, Dr Goble,' Pam said thoughtfully. 'So what do you suggest?'

'I think, Mrs Owen, that Nicola should drop one of her O level subjects. I also think it would be wise to impose some limit on the number of mornings she practises in her studio. Getting up so early every morning is too much when she has to work late at night on her homework.'

Ed and Pam agreed to see to this, feeling a little ashamed that it had never occurred to them that Nicola might have been working too hard.

'There's another thing, Mr Owen,' the psychiatrist continued. 'When I visited your house, I noticed that the branches of a large cherry tree were just touching the window of Nicola's bedroom. Sometimes at night, when there's a strong breeze blowing, the tips of the branches brush the windows and make noises that at times startle Nicola.'

'She's never mentioned it to me,' Ed declared. Then, turning to Pam, he asked, 'Has Nicola ever said anything to you about it?'

'No, never. How very strange.'

'I'll lop the branches back first thing tomorrow morning,' Ed said.

'And I'll see the headmistress as soon as I can,' Pam said, 'to discuss which subject Nicola can drop.'

Within a couple of days, all Dr Goble's suggestions had been implemented.

\*　　\*　　\*

Cutting down on my schoolwork and dancing practice didn't change anything. I was still very unsettled in myself and regularly experienced very low days when, for no reason, I would feel terribly depressed and just want to burst out crying. I often had bad headaches and I was starting to get very emotional over things. Previously, I'd always had masses of energy and determination, but I started having days when I felt totally lethargic and couldn't be bothered to do anything.

I also became even more of an exhibitionist at school after the other girls had discovered I was seeing a psychiatrist. I suppose I began to live up to their expectations of somebody who was something of a 'nutter'. I'd draw on my legs in class, rip my school dress and eat half a dozen bars of chocolate at break.

At home, I felt that Mum was watching me as though there might be something odd about me. So I became very critical of her. I was convinced she didn't look after Dad properly. I'd say things like, 'I know, Mum, that you want to do your own thing, but is it too much to ask to keep the house tidy? You know it's his pet hate to have the place in a mess. And why can't you have a meal ready when he comes home, especially as you don't work?'

This would inevitably lead to a row and I'd storm off to bed, but Mum's reaction only served to convince me that she was jealous of the special relationship that existed between Dad and me.

A few weeks after I'd overdosed on pills, I was invited out by a dark-haired, fresh-faced boy called Mark, who was a year older than me. He was my first boyfriend.

'Have you ever kissed anyone before?' he asked me.

'Loads of times!' I replied, although I never had.

The first kiss was mind-blowing stuff. I felt wonderful and our relationship rapidly became very intense. We progressed to heavy petting, but we only went that far and no further. I didn't do anything worse than any other girl, but I never felt totally right in the situation. I always felt that with Mark I was doing something wrong.

The trouble was that Dad used to make me feel very bad about going out with boys. It was as though he didn't quite trust Sally and me. So he was very strict on time-keeping and things like that. When talking about relationships with boys, his favourite saying was, 'Just remember that your body is a temple. Only let a genuine worshipper enter it.' When he said this, Sally would be killing herself with laughter, because she thought it was a load of rubbish, but I was really moved by it, feeling terribly privileged that Dad was talking to us as adults.

After a while, I wasn't very nice to Mark, I suppose. I used to dangle him on a piece of string. Sometimes I'd be loving and then the next time I'd be off-hand. I'd arrange to meet him and then not turn up. When I did go out with him, there were always men who found me very attractive and I loved flirting with them. After about four months, Mark and I stopped seeing each other. I didn't have another loving relationship with a man until I was eighteen.

But going out with Mark boosted my confidence. I started wearing quite outrageous clothes. It wasn't that I intended to be provocative. I merely wanted to dress in a distinctive style. For example, Mum made me a stunning patchwork skirt that I wore with a thin cotton vest. On one occasion, a guy invited me out and asked me not to go over the top with my clothes. Of course, that was the kiss of death! I wound my hair around a wire coat-hanger so that it stuck straight up and I borrowed one of my mum's old Sixties dresses. The poor boy was so put out that he found it difficult to speak to me all evening!

I liked to be stared at, to have people looking at me. It made me feel good. It was as though the need for adoration I'd once fulfilled by being on stage was starting to seep through to my everyday life as well. When I was a young child, I was so timid that most people weren't even aware of me. But all that had changed. Now everybody noticed me.

# CHAPTER FIVE

## *Sleeping with the Dead*

In the months leading up to her fifteenth birthday, aspects of Nicola's behaviour increasingly worried Pam. But, when she tried to discuss her concerns with Ed, he brushed them aside with, 'Oh, it's just growing up. It'll sort itself out,' or 'This is all nonsense. It's teenage stuff.' If she complained that Nicola wouldn't help with household chores such as washing-up, Ed would say, 'But it's your fault, Pamela. You should have made her do that when she was much younger. It's too late now.'

Sally, who was herself blossoming into a vivacious and attractive teenager, still greatly admired her elder sister and just assumed that Nicola's behaviour was part and parcel of being the dramatic person she was.

Johnnie, who was then ten, had a very different reaction to Nicola than the rest of his family. He found it extremely irritating that Nicola could dominate so much of the family scene. It seemed to him that both his parents were playing out their own frustrated theatricality through Nicola, readily basking in her reflected glory. There were times when he wished he could do something like playing the violin standing on his head, just so they'd notice him. But there was nothing he was particularly good at and so he knew he couldn't steal the show in any way. The position of star was already filled.

Perhaps it was because Johnnie was the most distant from Nicola that, although he kept his thoughts to himself, he was the first to be convinced that aspects of Nicola's behaviour were unacceptable. Neither he nor his sisters had ever helped themselves to food from the fridge or the larder, but when Nicola was baby-sitting, she began taking handfuls of biscuits from the larder and large bottles of bitter lemon from the drinks cabinet. When Johnnie asked what she was doing, Nicola would say she'd cleared it with her mum and dad. She encouraged both Sally and Johnnie to drink and eat, but it was she who always consumed the lion's share.

On one occasion, after Nicola had put him to bed, Johnnie crept downstairs and found her helping herself to some vodka. When she saw him, Nicola lost her temper and hit him, threatening the direst consequences if he said anything to their parents. He was the first to experience what was to become Nicola's frighteningly aggressive streak.

But Pam and Ed were soon to be presented with disturbing evidence that Nicola had ceased to be the model child. One Monday evening in mid-May, Ed was working at the bottom of the garden when he heard Pam shouting from the patio, 'Ed, Ed, come quickly!'

Hearing the urgency in her voice, he dropped the garden fork and ran towards her. 'What is it, Pam?' he asked. 'What's happening?'

Breathlessly, Pam explained, 'I went to collect Nicola from her dancing lesson to take her on to Dr Goble, but she's not there. She hasn't been to the class, although I dropped her off at Doreen Bird's at five o'clock. I talked to a couple of the girls there and one of them saw her going into Sidcup Railway Station. She thinks Nicola's gone to London.'

'What the hell is that bloody girl up to?' Ed exclaimed with an anger born of fear and the distress of seeing his wife's pretty face shot with pain.

'What shall we do, Ed?' she asked in despair.

'There's not a lot we can do at the moment, except inform the police.'

The duty officer at the local police station was used to dealing with enquiries about missing teenagers. Efficiently and sympathetically, he said, 'As there's no reason to suspect foul play, Mr Owen, we won't take any action for twenty-four hours. It's our experience that some girls of this age have hysterical outbursts for one reason or another and run off for the night. Nearly all of them are back home within twenty-four hours.'

'I see,' Ed said. 'But is there anything we can do now?'

'If I were you, sir, I'd ring around her friends and let their parents know what's happened. She may go there or contact one of them when she wants to return home.'

'Thank you. We'll do that.'

'One other thing, sir. I know this may sound silly but don't over-concern yourself at this stage. Almost certainly she's quite safe and will be back home with you tomorrow.'

'I hope you're right, officer. We're sick to our stomachs with worry.'

'I can understand that, sir.'

\* \* \*

For months, I'd been hiding food away in my room. Sometimes, I'd wake up in the middle of the night and feel very depressed, so I'd just eat and eat. Yet, at the same time, I was obsessed by a fear of putting on weight. So my mind wasn't right and my body wasn't right for dancing. All of a sudden, from being the best and the centre of attention, I was struggling a bit. I seemed to have lost the drive and determination I'd once had. I wasn't practising quite as much as I used to do either.

Mum must have suspected something, because as she was driving me to my dancing class, she said, 'Nicola, I never want you to feel you've been forced into this dancing. You know that if you don't want to do it, you can stop. It won't upset us. We want you to do what you want to do.'

I said nothing but, by the time she'd dropped me off, I felt panicky. I went into the dancing school and walked straight out again. Still wearing my school uniform with a black wrap-over woollen cardigan, I ran all the way to the station and bought a single ticket to central London.

When I arrived at London Bridge, I didn't have a clue where to go. I whizzed around on the buses for a while and then whizzed around on the underground. All the time, strange men were trying to chat me up. It wasn't a problem. I was so used to it. Indeed, I expected it. It was flattering and fed my ego. One man even stopped his car and said he'd thought of trying to knock me down so he could talk to me. Eventually, I went with one young man I'd met to a pub but, when it was clear I wasn't going to deliver what he wanted, he stormed off one way and I went another.

The area I found myself in was Bethnal Green and I wandered around, staring at the obvious poverty around me. It made me feel even more depressed. I didn't know what I could possibly have done that was wrong but I felt it was necessary for me to punish myself. Although I was terribly confused, I was sure I couldn't go home. There must have been some reason, I felt, why I'd run away.

Eventually, I walked into a small cemetery. It suited my mood. I wasn't at all frightened by the thought of sleeping among the dead. I had no fear of such things. I wasn't even afraid of what was happening to me, even though I kept asking myself, Why are you doing this? What's the point of it? Why are you doing all these weird things? But there was no answer I could give. I felt that I was on a roller-coaster and had no choice about what happened. I was just on it and I couldn't get off. It was as though somebody else had jumped into my body and was making me do things I didn't really want to do.

Finding a suitably flat gravestone, I lay down and tried to sleep. During the night, an old tramp shuffled up and, breathing methylated spirit fumes into my face, mumbled some incoherent words. I didn't reply and he staggered off, still mumbling, into the dark.

In the morning, I decided that I must find a job. First I went to Woolworth's and, using what little money I had left, I bought some make-up, which I then put on in a public toilet. Then I went to a nearby employment agency. I told them I was eighteen and a dancer but, as I'd broken my leg, I couldn't dance any more and needed a job. They readily accepted my story and sent me for an interview at a fashion warehouse in the East End. Even though I was wearing my school uniform, the man there thought I was suitable and gave me a job as a receptionist and model, starting the following Monday.

That was six days away and I had no money and nowhere to stay. So I went back to the employment agency, explained my situation and said, 'Look, can I have some temporary work until Monday?' They found me a job in another of their offices, just helping out, doing things like making the tea.

It was only after I'd finished my first day's work that I began to think about my parents and how distraught they would be. It felt as though the person who'd been occupying my body had suddenly gone, the old Nicola had returned and I was terrified at what my parents were going to say.

I decided to telephone my best friend at school. 'I've got myself into a bit of a mess, Gail,' I said. 'I've left home and I don't know what to do.'

She knew all about it, because Mum and Dad had spent most of the previous evening ringing my friends' parents, including hers. 'Look, Nicola,' she said, 'get on the train and come home. We'll meet you at the station.'

True to her word, Gail and her father were waiting for me at Sidcup Station. They took me back to their house, where I had a hot relaxing bath. Gail's father then phoned my parents.

'No, Mrs Owen,' I heard him say, 'she's absolutely fine and has clearly come to no harm. I hope you don't mind, but she was desperately hungry and my wife's just giving her some tea. We'll have her back within fifteen minutes.'

\*     \*     \*

When Pam heard from Gail's father, her major reaction was one of relief that Nicola had come to no harm. But she was also deeply worried and upset.

It was difficult for her to know how to deal with Nicola when she was brought back to the house. Pam didn't want to make matters worse, but she felt it was essential to point out what distress her daughter had caused.

'Your father's demented with worry,' she said.

'Where is he?' Nicola asked.

'Where do you think he is? He's in London combing the West End for you. I don't know what he'll say when he gets back.'

'I'm sorry, Mum. I really am.'

'We didn't know what had happened to you – where you'd gone. We informed the police that you were missing. I expect they'll want to talk to you. You've caused a lot of bother, Nicola. I don't know. I really don't know. What got into you, Nicola? What made you do it?'

'I wish I knew, Mum. Believe me, I honestly don't know. Some days, I just don't feel myself. I don't know why I did it.'

'Is it the dancing? Do you want to give it up?'

Nicola didn't reply. It was clearly a conversation that was leading nowhere and so Pam asked Nicola where she'd been and what she'd done. Relieved to be on surer ground, Nicola gave a jaunty and glossy account of her adventures. Pam listened in silence, astonished at her daughter's daring and saddened by her apparent lack of remorse. When Nicola had finished, she readily accepted Pam's suggestion that she should have an early night. While Nicola slept, Pam waited anxiously for Ed's return.

He arrived just after midnight to hear with initial disbelief that Nicola was fast asleep in her bed, safe and sound. Of course, he was relieved she had returned but, worn out and exhausted, he listened to Pam's retelling of Nicola's story with rising anger at the stupidity and incomprehensibility of the whole episode. He had spent a frustrating, even degrading, evening peering into coffee shops, ice-cream parlours, amusement arcades and shop doorways, stopping young men in the street to ask them if they recognized Nicola from a photograph and a piece of material that was the same as her school dress. All they got were false leads and a few ribald comments.

In the morning, Ed, finding it hard to control his anger, tried to discover from Nicola if she had any reason for running away from home. He desperately wanted to know, but she told him nothing. In the end, he concluded that the best thing to do was to carry on as though the incident had never happened.

For the next few weeks, he and Pam turned their minds to the preparations for Nicola's fifteenth birthday party.

'You can have about forty people,' Pam told Nicola. 'I'll lay on all the food and your dad and I will be around to keep an eye on everything.'

'No, you won't,' Nicola said. 'You'll have to be out of the house for the party.'

Pam didn't know what to do, but one of the group of young boys who frequently visited the house said to her, 'Mrs Owen, I think it'd be best for you to stay in that night.'

Worried by this, Pam told Nicola that she wanted to send all the guests written invitations, but Nicola seemed unwilling to provide their names and addresses.

Her parents realized why when the party started. By eight o'clock, over a hundred teenagers had arrived and were spilling out of the house into the garden. By quarter past eight, all the food and drink had been devoured and an ugly atmosphere was developing. Nicola had invited boys from two local rival schools – one was a private school and the other a state secondary school. It seemed inevitable that trouble would break out.

Ed stood determinedly in the crowded lounge, keeping a close watch on what was happening. Suddenly, he noticed Nicola, who was standing next to the piano talking to two boys. She was wearing a close-fitting, wine-coloured dress her mother had just bought her and, for the first time, Ed became aware that his young daughter had the body of a fully developed woman. Fleetingly he caught her eyes. Something about them was wrong. They seemed abnormally bright and startling. For a moment, he couldn't understand why they disturbed him so deeply. Then a feeling of intense nausea overwhelmed him as he realized he had seen that look once before. It was the same madness in Nicola's eyes that had so alarmed him when he'd watched her performing the witch's dance on stage. But, this time, the demented look of the witch had entered the family home.

He had no time to think more about it, because in a corner of the room the first fight had broken out. Ed sorted that out and then ordered a young couple out of the house for what he described as 'behaviour fit only for the bedroom'. Fortunately, at this point, three or four of Ed's and Pam's friends arrived to give them moral support and, after the rougher elements and the gatecrashers had been ejected, an enjoyable time was had by all the surviving guests. For much of the time, Nicola wasn't one of them. She had opted out with a splinter group of young men who sought the more certain supply of alcohol available in the local pub.

Immediately after her fifteenth birthday, Nicola announced that she absolutely refused to see the psychiatrist again. Dr Goble was extremely concerned about this, saying to Pam, 'She is emotionally a very sick girl, Mrs Owen, and her treatment must continue.' Neither Ed nor Pam accepted this and would not insist that Nicola changed her mind.

At this time, Nicola became close friends with Peter Kotting, one of the public school boys who'd attended her birthday party. Peter had been born badly deformed because his mother had contracted German measles when she was pregnant. He and Nicola got on well together. They were on the same wavelength and made each other laugh. They also had something else in common – strangers tended, for different reasons, to gawp at both of them. Mrs Kotting once heard Nicola say to her son, 'Let's go to the party together, Peter, and then we won't know which one of us they're staring at!'

That summer, Peter was taken into Queen Mary's Hospital, Roehampton to continue with what was to be a series of over thirty operations to straighten and extend his limbs. During his six-week stay in hospital, Nicola was one of the few people who visited him regularly. Most of his friends found it too horrendous to go to the hospital because there were so many badly deformed and injured people there. One young man had blown the front of his face off with a shotgun and had to wear a mask. Another had been in a car crash that had amputated the top of his head. There were also several armless or legless thalidomide victims.

But Nicola took it all in her stride. She would greet Peter with a kiss and then push him in his wheelchair down to the cafeteria where she'd chat to Peter's fellow patients. When Peter eventually came out of hospital, his jaw was wired up and so he wasn't able to eat and could drink only through a straw. Because of this, Nicola asked her mother to buy a liquidizer so that Peter could come and spend the day at their house. Both Peter and his parents saw Nicola as being a delightful girl who was very caring and loving.

During those summer months, Ed was delighted that Nicola seemed to have settled back into her normal way of life. But, as autumn approached, there were aspects of her daughter's behaviour that worried Pam. Nicola was no longer getting up at six in the morning to practise her dancing. She was also becoming far more moody. Sometimes, when people arrived at the house, she'd go to her room, saying, 'I've got a headache.' While Ed was away on business, she was increasingly rude to her mother. It was hard for Pam to explain her worries to Ed. When he was at home, Nicola was always extremely loving towards him.

'I'm getting a bit fed up with Nicola,' Pam would say. 'She's ever so rude to me, Ed.'

'Well, she's all right with me,' he'd say.

'But why don't you talk to her?'

'I can hardly deal with something that happens when I'm not here,' he'd reply, and that would be the end of the matter.

In October, it seemed there was a more important reason for Ed and Pam to be concerned about Nicola. Her appendix burst and she was rushed into hospital for an emergency operation. As Ed was away from home, it was Pam who went with her and told the ward sister that special care should be taken with Nicola because she'd already had many medical problems, including a collapsed lung and bronchial pneumonia.

When Pam arrived in the ward on the day after the operation, Nicola was in bed, crying. She told her mother that she couldn't cope with the pain in her side and a new pain in her chest. As Nicola wanted to go to the toilet, Pam called a nurse and asked for a bedpan.

'Now come on, Nicola,' the nurse said impatiently. 'Don't make a fuss. You can walk to the lavatory.'

Pam was incensed. 'She has a pain in her chest, nurse. There's obviously something wrong.'

The nurse was unmoved. 'That's all right,' she said. 'I'll help you, Nicola. Don't let's make a big thing out of it. There's a good girl.'

When Nicola arrived back from the bathroom, her appearance worried Pam. Feeling sure that her daughter was running a high temperature, she arranged with the sister to have a doctor take a look at Nicola. Her concern seemed unwarranted, because two days after the operation, Nicola was up and about, helping the nurses around the ward and receiving visits from her friends.

But the following day, when Pam arrived in the ward, she was met by the sister who said, 'Mrs Owen, we found Nicola in the toilet this morning. She had collapsed and coughed up blood. I'm afraid she's very ill.'

Worried and angry, Pam snapped, 'I've been trying to tell you she wasn't well. Why has Nicola been allowed to walk around the ward waiting on other patients? She never makes a fuss and because of that people have taken advantage of her.'

The sister did not respond to this, but said calmly, 'Nicola is now on strong antibiotics and a sedative. She's asleep and I don't think it's advisable for you to stay too long.'

That evening, when Ed returned, Pam told him what had happened. He drove immediately to the hospital and, in a lengthy meeting with the duty doctor, he forcibly expressed his dissatisfaction with the treatment Nicola had received. It obviously had some effect. From then on, a nurse or a doctor seemed to check on her hourly.

Although she was released from hospital a few days later, it was nearing Christmas before Nicola had completely recovered. Once again, it seemed to her that all the hard work she was putting in to become a dancer was constantly being frustrated by some obstacle or other.

When she had been taken ill, she had been rehearsing an *Annie Get Your Gun* dance for a choreography exhibition at her dancing school. Although still not fully fit, she did take part. Afterwards, the principal dancing teacher said to her, 'I've seen a lot of talented dancers in my time and I'm telling you that you could be a good ballet dancer, but you will only ever be that – a good ballet dancer. But, in the musical comedy field, you can go right to the top. You are so talented, I'm convinced you can be a second Shirley MacLaine.'

Such praise from a formidable and extremely experienced dancing teacher delighted Nicola's parents and confirmed her ambition to dedicate herself to become a professional dancer. In the New Year, however, she had to embark on a lengthy period of study and revision for her O level examinations which she was to sit in June. At least for those six months, her dancing would have to take second place.

But, as she cut back on her dancing exercise, she began to eat more and more. One day, Pam bought a large box of chocolates for Nicola to give a friend as a birthday present. In the morning when Nicola woke up, she ate them all and then went downstairs for a hearty breakfast. Any money she was given, or could steal, she spent in supermarkets buying sweets and junk food, even wolfing down tinned sponge puddings that should first have been cooked for thirty minutes. At home, she'd raid the larder and the fridge for anything that was edible.

At Easter, she went with a school party to Grenoble so that she could brush up her spoken French. To her horror, Nicola discovered that the family with whom she was to stay lived in a run-down, multi-racial tenement block. The lift was defaced with graffiti and stank of urine. There was only garden furniture in the lounge and her bedroom didn't have a window. She was constantly being reprimanded for spending too long in the bathroom or leaning out of a window to get some fresh air. Even more upsetting was the discovery that the family cat was kept shut up in a tiny broom cupboard. Miserable and homesick, Nicola took refuge in food. After her three week stay in France, she returned home weighing ten stone. Ed and Pam were astonished and upset when they saw how overweight Nicola was, but they were far angrier with the school and the French family than they were with their daughter.

As spring turned to summer, Nicola managed through self-induced vomiting and bouts of starvation to lose just over one of the two stone she'd gained during the previous twelve months. For the time being, Nicola hadn't quite lost the struggle to stay in control of her body.

# CHAPTER SIX

## *'I've been raped!'*

My parents had often told me, 'Don't walk through the woods by yourself. If you're with other people, that's all right. But, if you're on your own, take the long way round.'

But the long way round was such a drag and, of course, took so much more time.

After months of preparation, mock examinations and late-night revision, I took the first of my O levels on 7 June. Afterwards, wearing a green cotton dress that was the school's summer uniform and a pair of shoes with thick-wedged heels that were then the height of fashion, I caught the bus to Bexley. By the time I got off, I was feeling exhausted and so, as it was a glorious summer day, I set off on my own to take the short cut through the woods.

I entered Bexley Woods at the lower end by the narrow stream. From there, the wood rises steeply until the ancient trees abruptly come to an end at a long unbroken stretch of garden fences. A well-trodden, gravel-strewn path bisects the wood from the lower entrance to another in Camden Road that was only a hundred and fifty metres from our house.

I walked slowly up the steepest part of the path, trying desperately not to break an ankle by slipping on the loose gravel. I'd almost reached the top when, to my left, I saw a deeply sun-tanned man in a cream-coloured anorak, sitting spread-eagled on a bench. I did a double take because I suddenly realized that he was playing with his erect penis. I wasn't at all frightened and my first thought was, 'I can't wait to tell the girls at school about this!' As I passed him, I carefully stared straight ahead.

'Come and wank me off,' he shouted.

He kept on shouting and I walked as quickly as I could but it was impossible for me to run because of my stupid shoes. The safety of the Camden Road entrance was still some two hundred metres away.

Then I heard his heavy footsteps behind me. I was instantly terrified and desperately tried to run but, in seconds, he'd caught up with me and grabbed hold of me from the back. He hooked one arm around my neck and with his other hand held my left arm in a vice-like grip.

I couldn't believe there was nobody else around. Where were the women pushing their prams, the old men walking their dogs and the packs of young boys charging through the trees? At any minute, somebody would come along and save me.

I tried to scream, but only a squeak came out.

'If you make make a noise,' he hissed, 'I'll break your bloody arm.' Constantly saying filthy things, he dragged me off the path and into the wood. I was terrified that he was going to kill me. He pushed me up against a tree, thrust his penis into my hand and said, 'Touch it!' I really didn't know what he wanted me to do. He shouted abuse at me and grabbing my hand firmly, made me move it up and down his penis. With his body, he was pressing me against the tree and, with his other hand, he was desperately trying to pull down my knickers as he forced his penis towards me. Then, panting and cursing, he came over my school dress, pushed me brusquely aside and ran off through the woods.

I was shaking all over, but I was really relieved that I hadn't been killed. I'd been so scared that I didn't know what had actually happened. I was sure he'd been trying to penetrate me, but I'd had so little sexual experience that I didn't know if intercourse had taken place or not. All I knew was it had nothing to do with me and it wasn't my fault.

My legs were like jelly. I couldn't run. So I walked up the path towards the exit. When I reached it, I burst into tears.

Two painters were working on a house on the other side of the road. They saw me and one of them came over to me and said, 'What's the matter?'

'A man just . . .'

That was all he needed. 'Where?' he asked.

I pointed behind me and, with my words punctuated by sobs, I told him where it had happened. He shouted to his mate and ran off into the woods.

The other painter came over and took me back to the house where he made me a cup of tea and telephoned the police. After explaining what had happened, he handed me the receiver. I was asked only one question, 'Were you raped?'

It may sound unbelievable, but I honestly didn't know whether I'd been raped or not. I was very confused and didn't know what to say and so I didn't say anything. It was obviously decided that my silence meant I had been raped, because the policeman announced he was sending a police car round to the house so that we could go and search for the man.

I sat in the police car as we drove around the area looking for my assailant, but there was no sign of him. After half an hour I was driven home. By that time, all the terror had gone. I felt the sexual part hadn't been such a big thing. The biggest feeling I had was relief at still being alive.

Dad was in Durham on a business trip and, when we arrived at the house, Mum had gone to fetch Johnnie from school. The policeman waited for her to return. When she did, she saw the police car and assumed that something terrible had happened. Naturally, she was shocked and upset by the news. Knowing she was about to create a big production number out of the whole thing, I said, 'Mum, it's all right. Please don't make a fuss. I can't take any more fuss!'

I went upstairs and, as I'd been instructed, put all the clothes I'd been wearing into a plastic bag so they could be taken back to the police station. Then I climbed into the bath. As I lay there, I said to myself, 'I don't really care what's happened. It just doesn't matter any more.'

A little while later, two CID officers arrived – a man and a woman. They fired a battery of questions at me: 'You're a strong girl. Why didn't you defend yourself?', 'Was this man a friend of yours?', 'Why didn't you scream? Anybody can scream.'

Then the policewoman said, 'We think this is a case of rape, miss.'

'What would happen if it was?' I asked.

'You'd have to be examined by a doctor.'

That seemed to be a good idea and so I said, 'I think I'd better see a doctor.'

'So it was rape!' she said triumphantly.

'I suppose so,' I agreed.

Half an hour later, Mum took me to Bexleyheath Police Station where I was examined by a lady doctor. She said my hymen was stretched, but not broken. To be on the safe side, however, she gave me a birth-control pill.

When Dad returned home from his business trip, there was another bout of questions. I didn't want to talk about it, but both Mum and Dad seemed desperate for me to say that I hadn't been raped and kept on asking things like, 'Did you make it up to attract attention?' I still honestly didn't know what had happened but, in the end, it seemed easiest to go along with them and let them believe that I'd been lying.

The police, however, continued to think that I had been raped and later that week, on one of the days I wasn't taking an O level exam, I went to Scotland Yard and peered through thousands of photographs, trying to identify my attacker. But it was impossible. I couldn't remember his face – just that he was sun-tanned and swarthy-looking. Not surprisingly, the man was never traced.

For a few days, I'd been the centre of attention again, but then it was back to the grindstone of exams and the whole incident was treated as being best forgotten. Yet, though my initial feeling of shock had gone, it did seem to have affected me in unexpected ways. For no apparent reason, I'd suddenly fly into a rage. A week after the incident, I felt so angry when I came home from school that I ran up to my bedroom and hurled my china piggy bank at the dressing-room mirror so violently that it shattered.

Also, instead of dressing modestly to discourage another attack, I started to flaunt my body. On one occasion, I hitch-hiked home from the open-air swimming pool in my bikini. At the local disco, I created a sensation by embarking on a strip-tease. Wherever I went, I wore the shortest of skirts. Young men were always talking to me and asking me out, but they must have sensed there was something odd about me, because all of them rapidly lost interest. It seemed as though I often craved the attention I was given, but there were other times when I was totally withdrawn.

I was glad when the exams came to an end because a few weeks later I left school for good. I'd grown to hate it there and always seemed to be getting into trouble. Dad wanted me to stay on, because he really would have liked me to study modern languages at university, but I wasn't having any of that. I decided that I would become a full-time student at the dancing school I'd been attending in the evening – the Doreen Bird School of Acting and Dance. I'd never seriously thought of doing anything else but becoming a professional dancer.

After I'd left school, we went on holiday to Dorset. It was the first time for years that we hadn't gone abroad together. We stayed at a country pub where we enjoyed superb home cooking, such as large helpings of steamed pudding. But this still didn't provide me with enough to eat and so, when the others hurried off to the beach, I'd dawdle behind so I could nip into the village shop and buy massive quantities of sweets which I'd eat in some quiet corner before joining my family.

It was extremely hot that summer and I went really brown. One night at dinner, I was wearing a pair of tight jeans and, what with my tan and my curvaceous figure, I thought I was the bee's knees. As I looked appreciatively at my body, I found to my horror that there was a roll of flesh above the waistband of my jeans and I thought, 'This is the end. Everybody will notice I'm putting on weight again. How can I dance like this?'

I knew that I had to lose weight before I started my full-time dancing course in the autumn and so, when I returned home from Dorset, I went for five days without eating or touching a drop of alcohol. Then, deciding I must have lost my appetite, I started to eat again.

But the compulsion to keep on eating more and more was overwhelming. I filled a mixing bowl with Rice Krispies, put in two pints of milk and half a packet of sugar and ate it all. But it still wasn't enough. I then rapidly consumed a dozen slices of toast. After that, the only thing I could do was to make myself sick.

The cycle of gorging, being sick, fasting, gorging and being sick became firmly established as my normal way of life. Later, there were times when I'd made myself sick so often that I was bringing up blood, but that still didn't frighten me as much as the fact that I was putting on weight.

Late in August, Sally and I went to France for ten days to stay with some family friends in Normandy. It was still extremely hot and one day, as Sally and I were window-shopping in Rouen, I said to her, 'I wonder what it would be like in a French hospital.'

'What on earth are you talking about?'

'I was just wondering what would happen if I suddenly collapsed in the main street of Rouen,' I said. Then I fainted. So I found out what a French hospital was like

75

after all, although, after a few hours, I was discharged because nothing seemed to be wrong with me.

It was impossible for me to work out what had happened. Did I really feel faint because I'd been on a fast or because it was stiflingly hot? Did I say what I did to Sally only because I felt faint? Or was it because of what I'd said that I actually fainted – the thought being mother to the deed? Or did I just pretend to faint, wanting again to be the centre of attention? I found it impossible to give an honest answer. But I did know that, not for the first time, as the incident took place, I felt as though I was acting out a part on the stage. Yet it wasn't exactly that, because it was really as though I was watching myself, completely under somebody else's control, unable to stop my own actions.

*      *      *

When the two girls returned from Normandy, their anxious parents were desperate to hear about Nicola's latest exploit, but Sally, who was still very loyal to her sister, didn't repeat a word of what Nicola had said immediately before she'd fainted. Ed and Pam were extremely worried about what had happened until, two days later, their local doctor informed them that the X-rays sent on from the French hospital showed there was nothing physically wrong with Nicola.

That evening, Ed and Pam went to see friends in Rochester. They'd been there just over an hour when Sally phoned. 'As soon as you left, Nicola went out for a run,' she said, 'and she's not back yet. It's almost dark and I'm really worried. What shall I do, Mum?'

'I'm sure there's nothing to worry about,' Pam told her. 'Nicola's probably popped in to see one of her friends. She is naughty. But don't worry, Sally.'

'But she's only wearing your short, crocheted squash dress, Mum. Anything could have happened to her.'

76

'We'll leave right away, Sally,' Pam said reassuringly. 'We'll be back home in twenty minutes. Don't worry. We'll soon find her.'

Pam put down the phone and Ed anxiously demanded, 'What's that bloody girl done now?'

They hurried home. Nicola hadn't returned and so Pam began telephoning the hospitals in the area. At the third one, she was told there had been an emergency admission of a young woman who was apparently suffering from amnesia. About eighteen years old, she was wearing a short, white dress. 'Nicole' was engraved on a bracelet she was wearing.

Pam affirmed that this description matched her daughter and Ed immediately drove off to collect Nicola, even though the person on the phone said the hospital would prefer to keep her in overnight for observation.

When he arrived, Ed was shown to the bed where Nicola was lying with her eyes closed. A young doctor standing there looked apprehensively at Ed when he announced he was the girl's father and had come to take her home.

At that point, Nicola opened her eyes and said, 'Oh, hello. Where am I?'

This was too much like play-acting for Ed. 'Don't sod me around, Nicola!' he exploded. 'I'm your father. You know bloody well where you are!'

The young doctor stepped forward as though trying to come between his patient and her outraged father.

Ed looked him straight in the eyes and said, 'She's just playing the fool, doctor. I'm not having her wasting your time or taking up a useful hospital bed. I'm taking her home, but quick.'

Nicola's eyes were again firmly closed.

The doctor said icily to Ed, 'I'll decide what happens to my patient. You say you're this young woman's father . . .'

'Well, who the hell do you think I am? It was my wife who telephoned this hospital and tracked her down.'

'You do appreciate that this girl was found collapsed beside the road? It seems likely that she was thrown out of a car travelling from London and has suffered from some form of amnesia.'

'Amnesia be damned. Only last week, she tried to pull a similar stunt in Rouen. Our doctor's just had her X-rays through and there was nothing wrong with her.' Then realizing he was being unnecessarily aggressive, Ed simmered down a little and said, 'Look, I'm sorry if I seem angry, doctor. Please understand that my wife and I have just about had it up to here with Nicola. If you don't mind, I'd like to take her home now.'

'I understand, Mr Owen,' the doctor said sympathetically, 'but I still want to keep her here overnight for observation.'

As there was nothing more to be said, Ed left the hospital. 'What really got me,' he told Pam when he'd returned home, 'was that a young girl is found by the roadside wearing a short crocheted dress and then they concoct this wonderful theory about some hoods hurling her from a car. Where do they come up with such things?'

Pam saw the funny side of this and, laughing, said, 'I suppose they thought you were one of the toughies calling back to pick up the booty!'

Ed smiled. 'Perhaps they did,' he said. 'No wonder the doctor was so dubious when I said I was her father!'

As her parents talked downstairs, Sally lay in her bed, unable to sleep. There was something she felt she ought to talk to them about – something concerning Nicola. Although she felt a deep sense of loyalty to her sister, she felt her parents ought to know just how much Nicola was drinking. Having made up her mind to tell them, she went downstairs. But, as soon as she walked into the sitting-room, her resolve melted away.

'Oh, my poor Sally,' Pam said. 'Come and sit next to me. I'm not surprised you can't sleep with all this going on. Come and have a cuddle.'

Ed went off to the kitchen and, when he returned with the tea tray, asked Sally if she knew what was behind Nicola's fainting tricks.

'Not really, Dad,' Sally replied. 'Nicola's a bit odd at times and she's always showing off.'

'What do you mean, Sally?' Ed asked. 'In what way is she showing off?'

Having been put on the spot, Sally did her best to wriggle out of giving the answer. 'Well, nothing very specific, Dad. You know. It's just the way she behaves and the way she is with friends. She's always wanting to be centre stage.'

Pam tried a few more questions but Sally apparently had nothing more concrete to say.

When Nicola was collected the following morning, she was reluctant to talk about what had happened, but there was no suggestion that her memory was in any way impaired. It was, however, agreed that she would resume her regular visits to Dr Goble, the psychiatrist she'd first seen after taking an overdose.

Ed and Pam spent many hours discussing how best to deal with Nicola. Ed was still inclined to think his wife wasn't making sufficient allowances for the fact that Nicola was growing up and starting to think for herself.

Pam was convinced there was more to it than that. 'Nicola was never any trouble when she was a young girl, Eddie,' she said. Then voicing an idea that had been forming in her mind for a while, she added, 'She only started to be rude and do strange things after her periods started.'

'Well, that's no surprise,' Ed said dismissively. 'That's when she was changing from a girl into a woman. It's a difficult time. She'll grow out of it. At least, I bloody well hope she will.'

Ed felt sure the answer to these temporary difficulties was to treat Nicola more as an adult and encourage her to be more responsible. As she'd left school and was about to start as a full-time student at the dancing school, he said he'd open a bank account for her and give her a generous allowance of £33 a month.

Pam readily went along with this, but she was far from certain that Ed's scheme would provide the solution to Nicola's problems.

# CHAPTER SEVEN

## *Losing Hold on Life*

In the September that Nicola became a full-time student at the dancing school, Johnnie, who was eleven, became a boarder at his private school. He loved his parents, but he was really glad to get away from everything that was happening at home. He hated the friction and the arguments, which were getting more frequent. There always seemed to be some big commotion because of something Nicola had done. Many times, he'd lain in bed, crying, hoping that everything would be better in the morning.

As Nicola's weight increased and her enthusiasm for dancing began to wane, it became impossible to ignore the rising level of tension in the house. It was always associated with Nicola but, though they all might see her as being its primary cause, the rest of the family were also inclined to blame each other.

Johnnie thought his mother and father mishandled the situation. He felt that his mum was over-emotional in her dealings with Nicola, so that the smallest incident tended to be blown out of all proportion. His dad he saw as coping with things slightly better, even though he tended to lose his temper.

Sally saw her mother differently. In any difficulty with Nicola, she thought of her mum as being a calming influence, behaving in a very level-headed way and constantly trying, by showing ever more love, to rectify things. On the other hand, she felt her dad was reluctant to believe there were aspects of Nicola's behaviour that were deeply worrying.

Pam was concerned that Ed didn't appear to be giving her the support she needed, seeming to take Nicola's side in what was increasingly becoming a conflict between mother and daughter. The problem was made worse because Nicola adored her father, was afraid of his wrath and desperately wanted his approval. So she always gave him a lot of flattering attention when he was at home.

In any case, it was impossible for Pam to pinpoint exactly what was wrong with Nicola. There were always times when she behaved perfectly. As a result, family friends who didn't see her often tended, like Ed, to think that Pam was worrying too much about Nicola.

But Pam had good reason for her concern. Several times, when she was cleaning Nicola's extremely untidy room, she found enormous piles of cake and sweet wrappings, empty food tins and crisp packets under the bed. On one occasion, when taxed about this, Nicola flew into a rage, picked up a kitchen knife and started waving it at her mother. Sally rushed up and pulled her sister away, but not before Nicola had hurled the knife at Pam who, having dodged the missile, quietly sobbed, 'Oh, Nicola, Nicola. What are you doing?' Nicola neither replied nor seemed affected by her mother's tears.

As Nicola's behaviour became more and more unpredictable, Pam and Sally entered into a pact that they would not tell Ed about any of the incidents that happened while he was away on one of his many business trips. There seemed little point in doing so. He was always reluctant to accept that anything was really wrong and seemed to suspect that Pam was exaggerating.

In any case, there was little or nothing he could do – he couldn't prevent something that had already happened. So, when he phoned home, he was always told that Nicola had been on her best behaviour and that everything was fine.

Pam, however, found it increasingly difficult to deal with Nicola and with the tension that was building up between herself and Ed. On one occasion when Ed was going to be at home, she decided to take a break and visit her parents for a few days.

Ed readily agreed to this. He was delighted, when he got back to the house, to be greeted by Nicola saying, 'I've got the meal ready for you, Dad, and I've made you a cup of tea. Just sit down and I'll bring it all to you.'

'This is wonderful,' Ed thought. 'Nicola's being a super grown-up daughter. I like this.'

His attitude changed a few weeks later, when Pam went away again. On this occasion, Nicola had not only prepared the meal, she was also wearing one of her mother's dresses. When Ed demanded to know what she was doing, Nicola replied, 'Don't you think it suits me?'

Ed was incensed. 'Don't take bloody liberties, Nicola,' he shouted. At this, she burst into tears and Ed, more calmly, asked, 'Did your mum say you could wear it?'

'It's only an old thing,' she whimpered.

'I don't care. Go and take it off right now.'

For the first time, Ed had a sense of unease. Although he knew it wasn't unusual for girls to wear their mother's clothes and that Nicola was always swopping dresses with her sister, he felt it was more than possible that, in some strange way, Nicola was trying to usurp his wife's role.

*　　*　　*

After I started my full-time dancing course, my excessive eating became a major problem. I would eat and eat and eat. I'd eat last thing at night and, as soon as I woke up, I'd start eating again.

An almighty row blew up one night after my mother had discovered a pile of empty cans and boxes of chocolates stuffed under my bed. Dad dragged me on to the bathroom scales. 'Look at this, Pam,' he shouted. 'She's nine and a half stone. It's unbelievable. What the hell are you doing to yourself, Nicola?'

After that, he evolved a reward scheme by which he would add five pounds to my monthly allowance for every four pounds of weight that I lost.

Once again, I went on a starvation diet. After a few days, I arrived home and, finding everybody was out, I went into the kitchen and gorged myself on all the food I could find. That evening, some visitors called to see my parents. Mum offered them tea and a slice of cake. She went to the larder to take out the cake she'd just bought as part of her weekend shopping, but it wasn't there. Later, she came up to my room and asked me if I knew anything about it.

'No, I haven't had it,' I lied. 'I haven't even seen the cake.'

But so much food had disappeared over the months that my parents decided to stop it happening any more by locking the week's groceries in the office filing cabinet. When Mum told me this, I shouted and screamed hysterically, saying that I was constantly being watched and nobody trusted me.

Yet I still wanted to lose weight. I was hung-up on the belief that, if I did, everything would be all right. As I saw it, all my antisocial behaviour was only the result of my being overweight. I really hated being fat. I wasn't like my sister. Although she was overweight, she was still attractive. She still took a lot of trouble with her make-up and was concerned about her clothes. But, because I was putting on weight, I was becoming uglier and uglier and so I didn't put on any make-up or care what I wore. I really hated the way I looked.

Wearing a skimpy leotard meant that every bulge showed. Because of this, I felt I didn't want to go to dancing classes. Some days, instead of going to the school, I'd just walk around the streets – always walking and gorging myself on junk food. When Mum found out I'd been skiving off, there was another row.

We were always having slanging matches. I felt a lot of animosity towards Mum. I really didn't like her at all. It wasn't just that I thought she was giving Dad a raw deal and arguing with him all the time, it was also that she was forever trying to control my eating by poking around in my room when I wasn't there, keeping all the food locked away and constantly telling me I was putting on weight. She was no help at all.

More and more, I was becoming depressed, asking myself, Why am I doing this? Why am I destroying everything I have? Why, when supposedly everything's going so well for me, do I want to wreck it? I couldn't understand myself. I just felt a dreadful despair at knowing things weren't right, that they were going to get a lot worse and that I was powerless to do anything about it.

In an effort to blank out my despair, I started drinking heavily. My parents were very sociable so there was always drink in the house. For years, I'd been helping myself to their drink, topping up the gin and whisky with water so it wouldn't be noticed. But once Dad started giving me an allowance, I was able to buy my own. I enjoyed going into pubs alone and, much to the astonishment of the bar staff, downing several pints of beer in quick succession.

Yet, despite my excessive drinking and eating, I was still a talented dancer. At the end of my first term, I passed four examinations with good marks. I also successfully auditioned for the part of the principal boy in a local pantomime.

For this, I lost weight with determination and was considered a great success in the show which started on Boxing Day and ran for three weeks. It was my first professional dancing engagement and I should have felt good about it, but I didn't. I did silly things. For instance, at one performance I blackened out some of my front teeth. Nothing seemed right and I felt that I'd lost the desire to be a dancer. Even my enthusiasm for life seemed to be seeping away.

After the pantomime, things became even worse. As I retreated more and more into myself, the resentment I felt towards everybody else increased. Nobody and nothing seemed to be helping me. Early in February, I rang Dr Goble, the psychiatrist, and said I couldn't see any point in seeing him any more.

Most of my lunch-times and evenings were spent in pubs, drinking on my own. Somehow or other, my parents didn't notice I was often drunk, although once I rushed up to my room as soon as I came in and was sick all over my bed. As a punishment, Dad wouldn't allow me to go out for a week. After that, I decided to get a job as a barmaid. It wasn't difficult because, while I knew I was overweight, men looked on me as being well-endowed. I didn't survive at the pub for long. Within a couple of months I was sacked for stealing money from the till.

As I was spending so much on food and drink, I was always short of money. By May, I was not only overdrawn at the bank but I owed Mum over fifty pounds. I knew she wouldn't lend me any more and so I decided that, in another desperate effort to lose weight and change my way of life, I'd go on a prolonged fast. I lost a lot of weight and Dad was really pleased with me.

The dancing school had arranged an evening theatre outing after classes. As I was leaving home, Mum gave me a five-pound note and said, 'This is for you, Nicola. Use it to buy yourself a proper meal.'

All morning, during my dancing classes, I could think of nothing but food. As I walked out of the school at lunch-time, I thought to myself, You're going to start bingeing again, Nicola. You can't cope with it. You've no control over yourself. You were once so determined and ambitious – now you can't even manage to keep to a sensible diet.

So I decided I would do something about it. I went into Woolworth's and bought a packet of weed-killer. In a nearby café, I bought a piece of bread pudding and a can of coke. Then I went back to the dressing-room in the dance school. I cut the bread pudding open, sprinkled weed-killer all over the inside and then closed it again. I opened the can of coke and sprinkled in more of the weed-killer.

I'd just started eating the bread pudding, when a group of my dancing friends walked in.

'What's the matter with you, Nicola?' one asked. 'Aren't you feeling well?'

'Look, leave me alone, will you?' I snapped. 'I'm busy.'

Puzzled, they looked at each other and then one of them said, 'What's wrong with you, Nicola? What are you doing?'

'I'm just taking some weed-killer. I'll be all right in a minute.'

The girls sprang into action. Some grabbed the food and the coke, while others dragged me, protesting, to the dance teacher, who said I had to be taken to hospital. All the time I was saying, 'Please don't tell my parents. They'll be so angry. Promise me you won't tell my parents.' But, of course, I knew that the first thing they'd do was to telephone them.

As soon as I arrived at the hospital, I was taken to have my stomach pumped. I was laid out on a stretcher-bed and held down by a couple of brawny nurses. A tube was forced down my throat. I panicked. It was a massive tube that seemed to go on for ever and all the time I was retching and gagging. Then the contents of my stomach were sucked out so they could be examined. Finally, the tube was pulled out. The pain was excruciating and my throat was sore for days.

All the time I was thinking, This isn't me. Where's Nicola? Where has Nicola gone? I don't want to be this mad girl. Please help me. Why can't somebody help me?

\*   \*   \*

Pam was close to tears as she and Ed got back into the car after visiting Nicola in hospital.

'I just don't understand it any more, Ed,' Pam said. 'One minute she's trying to kill herself and the next she's sitting up in bed looking beautiful and breezily saying, "Oh, hello, Mum." I don't know, Ed. I just don't know any more.'

She started to cry and Ed, trying to comfort her, said, 'Now come on, Pam. We're both tired and it looks much worse than it really is.'

'I'm so frightened, Ed. You're away most of the time and I'm at home just waiting for the next incident. She's not our daughter any more. Look what she's doing to us. We're all rowing and arguing. What's happening to Nicola is happening to us. It's like living in hell. There's no peace and I don't know how much more of this I can stand!'

'It's not as bad as all that, Pam. We'll find a way to sort it out. I'm sure we will.'

'I wish we could. I think that girl is ill, very ill, but you just won't believe it. I don't think you can come to terms with not having the perfect family.'

'Don't talk so bloody daft, woman.'

'I'm not talking daft and I'm not a bloody woman. I'm your wife, Ed Owen, and I love Nicola. But you're not listening to me. There's something terribly wrong with her and I'm so frightened. When you're away, you just don't know how frightened I am.'

Ed might have been the last to admit it, but the once happy Owen family was in profound disarray.

\*　　\*　　\*

The day after I'd been admitted to the hospital, a Dr Sangster came to see me.

'I've been reading your case notes, Nicola,' he said in a most relaxed and friendly way. 'I just don't understand what this is all about. You seem to have everything going for you, but all I see in the medical records is a girl making a complete mess of her life. I want you to tell me about . . . to tell me all about it.'

I was feeling rested and would have quite liked talking to this tall, attractive man, but there was nothing I could say in response and so I merely looked away.

'I can see no reason why you should remotely consider eating weed-killer,' he went on. 'Was it a prank? Was it for a bet? It makes no sense. It's such a stupid thing to do.'

'I know,' I replied. 'It is ridiculous. I don't know what came over me. I just do these things.' He seemed upset that I hadn't opened up and confided in him. But what could I say?

Dr Sangster's expression became sterner as he said, 'When your mother comes to visit you today, would you tell her to have a word with the sister. I would like to meet both your parents for a chat. We've got to sort you out, Nicola. We just can't have this kind of silly behaviour.'

\*　　\*　　\*

Some days later, Pam and Ed kept an appointment with Dr Sangster at the hospital. Sitting in his cramped consulting-room, they answered many questions about Nicola's complex medical history and heard with relief that apparently she had taken little or no weed-killer.

'However, I'm going to keep her here for a few more days,' Dr Sangster said, 'if for no other reason than to give you two good people a bit of a rest.' Turning to Pam, he then asked, 'What is your feeling about Nicola, Mrs Owen?'

'I'm fed up with her. We've had enough.'

'Really? I found her quite charming.'

'She is. But it's so very upsetting and worrying that she keeps on doing these terrible things.'

'I'm sure it is, but I really don't think she's trying to kill herself. It may sound trite to say so, but I'm sure her suicide attempts are a cry for help. My worry is that, one of these times, she could kill herself accidentally. To prevent that, we must find out what her problem is. Have you any idea, Mrs Owen?'

'Ed doesn't agree with me,' Pam said, 'but I think it's something to do with her periods. As soon as they started, so did all this.'

Dr Sangster peered at her searchingly for a moment and then flipped through some medical records. 'I'd like Nicola to see our gynaecologist,' he said at last, 'to find out what he can tell us.'

'What do you think's wrong with her, doctor?' Ed asked, for the first time admitting that his daughter's behaviour wasn't normal.

'Frankly, Mr Owen, I don't know. Mrs Owen may be right in thinking there is something medically wrong, but it's also possible there may be a psychological problem. So we'll explore both avenues. That's why I want the gynaecologist to see her and I'll also fix up an appointment for you to visit an excellent adolescent psychiatric unit. Leave it to me.'

Ed and Pam felt relieved and grateful. It seemed at last that somebody was going to do something to help Nicola.

Unfortunately, however, the gynaecologist had a very long waiting list and nothing was heard from him. An appointment was made with the adolescent unit at the psychiatric hospital, but not until the middle of August – nearly three months away.

# CHAPTER EIGHT

## *No Way to Escape*

After I'd been released from hospital I felt so lethargic that even getting up in the morning took an enormous effort. I just wanted to eat and sleep all the time. Because I knew I looked awful, I didn't want to go out in the evenings. I wasn't very good with people. My eyes were cold and glazed. There was a weird aura about me that others seemed to detect. Even my sister started to give me a wide berth. Unlike me, she had her own large circle of friends, including a succession of boys who doted on her.

Because I was so strange, the other students at the dancing school also kept their distance from me. I hated being with them and seeing their cold, suspicious glances. The combination of this and my ever increasing weight made it impossible for me to continue with my classes. So, unbeknown to my parents, I stopped going. Instead, I'd wander the streets, drink in pubs, sit in a field aimlessly watching the ponies – that sort of thing. One day, Mrs Green, Mum's daily help, found me huddled on a seat in Bexley Woods, reading a book. She took me home and there was yet another almighty row. I was in the doghouse again, but I was used to that.

At home, it felt as though there was always an electrical charge in the air and that at any minute there'd be a terrific explosion. When it came, the charge would disappear for a short while before rapidly building up again. Mum and

Dad always seemed to be arguing and I had no rapport with them any more. I became totally convinced that if I could live in London, away from home, everything would be all right.

Eventually, I managed to persuade Mum and Dad that I should leave my dancing school and go to one in London.

When I told my dancing teacher what I intended to do, she was exasperated with me. 'It's no better in London,' she told me. 'It's you that's the problem, Nicola. You've got to sort yourself out. You can't run away from yourself.'

I didn't see it that way. I felt everything would be better in London. I was accepted by the Arts Education Trust School for a course starting in September, but, at my audition, the lecturer said, 'Listen, you need to lose some weight.'

'I know,' I replied. 'I've recently put a bit on and I'll lose it before I start. It's not a problem.'

But it was. Eating and drinking in large quantities had become an unshakeable obsession. Each time I gorged was another brick in the wall of self-loathing. At times, I had attacks of panic and hated what I'd become. But usually I felt exhausted and could only think, Well, why worry? I don't care any more. All I wanted to do was to sleep, day in and day out. When I wasn't sleeping, I found some escape by reading the gory pulp novels I'd started buying. I spent hours in bed just wishing I was in a room where no-one would come in and nag me.

That wasn't possible at home. Mum was forever wandering into my bedroom to see if I was all right. Her sneaky spot checks drove me wild. I'd shout and scream at her telling her to get the hell out of my room. Several times, I was so incensed that I jumped off the bed and chased her out. I desperately wanted to hit her, punish her. Why couldn't she leave me alone?

Early in July, just after my seventeenth birthday, I decided I couldn't stand being at home any longer. I drew out all the money I had in the bank and, immediately afterwards, I went to another branch and drew out a similar amount. I then ran away to Brighton where I found a grotty boarding-house where I could stay. Although I hated myself and the way I looked, I must still have been fairly attractive, or so the young Italian at the reception desk must have thought. He spent hours chatting to me. But most of the time I just sat alone on the beach, thinking, What am I going to do with my life? Why am I feeling so depressed? What is wrong with me? Somebody must know, but nobody so far has even touched the truth.

After four days in Brighton, I caught the train back to Albany Park. From the station, I rang an old friend and told her how terrified I was by what my parents might do and say. She arrived with her boyfriend and took me to her house from where she telephoned Mum and then drove me home. I was very calm and collected, ready to ignore any grilling or verbal attacks, but Mum and Dad seemed more relieved than angry.

Later, they said that we all needed a holiday and so they'd booked for the whole family to spend a fortnight in August at a hotel in Majorca. This meant that we'd be away for the first appointment at the adolescent unit and so it had to be postponed.

'You'll enjoy the holiday, Nicola,' Dad said. 'The hotel's on the beach and it has a disco. It'll be just like the great family holidays we used to have.'

I hated the idea. I was convinced it was the tension in the family that was making me feel ill. I felt I couldn't possibly go on holiday with Mum and Dad when I'd begun to resent both of them so much. They seemed to have such an incredible hold on me. They were dominating my life so much and I just wanted to be rid of them. I'd stopped dancing and didn't want to be motivated by them any more. They weren't going to push me around ever again.

I decided that, rather than going away on holiday, I would leave home for good. In London, I found a small bed-sit in New Cross and a job working in MacDonald's which was due to start on the day we were supposed to be flying to Majorca.

When I returned home, Mum was out. I took a large suitcase to my room and began to pack. In went not only the bed linen and saucepans I needed, but also some antique china plates my mother had collected over the years. She was always boasting about how valuable they were and so I thought I'd sell them to raise enough cash to fund myself until I'd earned my first week's wage.

I'd almost finished packing when Mum walked into my room. Seeing the full suitcase lying open on the bed, she said, 'What are you doing, Nicola?'

'I'm leaving home.'

'What do you mean?'

'What I said. I'm leaving home.'

Mum peered into the case and said, 'Well, you can't take my sheets!' She pulled them out and threw them out of the room. Then she saw her plates and really lost her temper. She picked the case up and starting emptying everything on to the bed, screaming, 'You can't take this! You can't take that!'

She was even saying that I couldn't take my clothes and so I shouted back, 'How dare you encroach on my privacy! How dare you unpack my stuff and tell me this belongs to you and that belongs to you!' In my fury, I started pulling out the drawers in my room and emptying the contents on the floor, screaming, 'You said this was my home. If those things don't belong to me, what do I have that's mine? What do I own?' Then picking up one thing after another, I kept on saying, 'Is this mine? Is this mine? Is this mine?'

Grabbing one of the pulp novels I'd been reading, Mum shouted, 'These are yours, for a start. These are certainly yours. Just look at them. They're awful. They're violent and they're disgusting. These are yours and they shouldn't be in this house.' Then she stormed off with the book and her plates. A few minutes later, she was back again, saying, 'Your father wants to have a word with you.'

I went downstairs and into the office. I could see immediately that Mum had managed to whip Dad up into a frenzy. She was hovering expectantly by his desk like a tricoteuse at the guillotine.

Dad launched into a diatribe on everything I'd been doing wrong – my laziness, stealing Mum's precious plates, getting drunk, the disgusting books I was reading, the terrible worry I was causing them both, my eating habits and even the length of time I spent in the bathroom. 'Why are you doing all these things?' he demanded. 'Why? What's wrong with you? Why are you running away this time?'

'I'm leaving home. I've got myself a flat and I've got myself a job and that's what I'm going to do.'

'Why?'

'I just don't want to go away on holiday with you.'

'I don't care a sod what you want or you don't want, Nicola. You're not leaving home. You're bloody well going on holiday with us and that's my final word.'

With all the venom I could muster, I said, 'You'll regret this!'

Momentarily, I saw a flash of fear in his eyes.

'Can I go now?' I said. 'I'm taking the dog for a walk.'

'All right, Nicola,' he said, his hectoring tone totally dissipated. 'We're going to have a great holiday. Everything's going to be fine.'

Leaving Mum and Dad in the office, I went to the kitchen, took a five-pound note from Mum's bag and attached the lead to Lizzie's collar. I walked her straight through the woods to the off-licence. I bought two bottles of sherry and returned with them to the woods. Sitting on a wooden bench close to the stream, I quickly drank the entire contents of one bottle and started on the next. When I couldn't gulp down any more, I threw the bottles into the river with such an anger, directed not at my parents, but at myself. It wasn't them that I hated, but what I'd become.

I hurried home, put Lizzie in the kitchen and walked upstairs. Perhaps because of all the food I was eating, I seemed to have built up an immunity to alcohol. I didn't feel drunk, but inside I was hysterical. I went into the bathroom opposite my bedroom and locked the door. I stared at my reflection in the mirror of the bathroom cabinet and thought, I hate you. I hate you for what you're doing to me. I'm going to punish you for all the worry you caused your parents. I'm going to punish you for once having been a beautiful young girl. I'm going to punish you.

Opening the cabinet, I took out a pair of scissors and fascinated, as though I was watching someone else's actions, I began to hack off my long, golden hair until all that remained was a short stubble. I stared at myself in the mirror. Not at all shocked by what I saw, I started giggling. Now you are mad! I thought. Now you're really mad!

I wrapped a towel around my head, unlocked the bathroom door and walked into my sister's bedroom. As she looked up, I said, 'Oh, look, Sal. I've given myself a bit of a haircut.' I pulled off the towel and started laughing.

Sally screamed, burst into tears and gasped, 'Oh, Nicola, what on earth have you done? What have you done that for?' Then she ran to the door and shouted, 'Mum! Dad!'

They ran up the stairs and came rushing into Sally's room. I was sitting on her bed, still laughing. When he saw me, Dad screamed, 'What the bloody hell have you done now?' and burst into tears. It was the first time I'd ever seen him cry. He went into the bathroom and gathered all my hair into a paper bag. Mum was clearly in a state of shock. She kept staring at my head, saying, 'Oh, Nicola! Such lovely hair! Oh, Nicola!'

I felt unmoved by it all. I didn't like myself and didn't care a damn any more. If I couldn't be good, I might as well be as horrible as I could. Everyone was distraught, but I thought, What's the big deal? It's my hair. Why are they making such a fuss?

Dad came back in the room to say he'd phoned the doctor and was going to fetch a sedative for me from the surgery.

As he left, Mum said, 'Come on, Nicola. I'll help you tidy up your room.' It had been in a terrible mess even before I'd flung out the contents of my drawers all over the bed and the floor.

When Dad returned, he gave me the sedative and then helped with the tidying up. It took nearly an hour to put everything neatly away and change all the bedclothes.

By that time, I was beginning to feel drowsy and so Mum tucked me into bed, kissed me and said, 'Nick, don't worry. It's all going to be all right. Good night.' She and Dad then left the room, gently closing the door.

For a while, I lay in the darkness thinking, I still hate myself, I still hate myself. In the grip of this obsession, I quietly got out of bed, went back into the bathroom, locked the door, picked up a razor and carefully shaved my whole head. Next I shaved off my eyebrows. Then I took the scissors and cut off all my eyelashes.

As I was coming out of the bathroom, I was seen by Sally who gawped at me in silent horror. I ignored her, climbed back into bed and instantly fell asleep.

I woke about half-past two the next afternoon in my parents' bed. Apparently, Dad had carried me there after Sally had called them for the second time. Mum had been awake all night on guard-duty in case I attempted to do anything else.

Mum helped me dress and gave me a scarf to wrap round my head. Then she took me downstairs. The local doctor and Dr Sangster from the hospital were sitting side by side in the lounge. They were very sharp with me.

'You've gone too far this time, Nicola,' Dr Sangster said. 'You've got to realize that, if there is just one further incident, there is every likelihood you will be sent to a mental hospital.'

'I don't care,' I said truthfully.

The following day, with a scarf round my head, pencilled in eyebrows and sunglasses, I went with Mum to Selfridges in London to buy a wig. Mum told the very discreet shop assistant a pack of lies about my having spilt paint on my head and then I tried on a whole range of wigs. I'd always wanted very long hair and so I chose the longest wig, which hung down below my waist. The hair was very dark, nothing like my own. Mum then bought me some false eyelashes.

Wearing these and my new wig, I walked with Mum down Oxford Street. 'What do you think of that?' she said in amazement. 'Those young men we've just passed were actually giving you the eye!'

By the evening, I was beginning to feel that the old Nicola had returned and I sat down with Dad to have one of our heart-to-heart chats. He kept trying to discover what had made me shave off all my hair.

'Dad, it's as if there was another person and I was just watching, powerless to do anything,' I said.

'But you can't have known what you were doing,' Dad said.

'I did, Dad. I knew exactly what I was doing, but I'm trying to tell you it was as though it was somebody else. It was all very clear.'

Dad was too emotionally involved with me to comprehend this. He kept on approaching everything from the wrong direction. 'Why, when we've given you everything you ever wanted,' he asked me, 'do you repay us by doing things like this?'

'Dad, I can't help it. Can't you understand? I don't know. I've got no answer. I wish I had. I don't want to do these things, but I can't help it.'

A few days later, I went on the family holiday after all and I hated it. The first week wasn't too bad, but then I began to feel the others were treating me as though I was really weird and so, escaping from them, I spent a lot of time drinking Bacardi and coke. One night, I was so drunk I threw up all over the bedroom. Mum and Dad cleared up all the mess and washed the bed clothes, hanging them over the balcony to dry.

I deliberately lay in the sun until I'd badly burnt my chest but, despite that, I still sunbathed to burn myself more. I had a perverse pleasure in punishing myself because I felt I deserved it. I was a nasty little girl. I had gone so far that there was no chance I was going to be good any more. So I wanted to be really bad.

The longer the holiday lasted, the more antagonistic I felt towards everybody. One night, we were having dinner in a posh restaurant overlooking the bay. Johnnie had been sounding off about animal rights and how cruel it was for women to wear fur coats. It was a favourite topic of his and Mum's.

I sliced off a chunk of veal and said, 'I don't care what you say, Johnnie. Animals are on this earth for our use. Why should the senseless creatures have any rights?'

Johnnie was very upset. He jumped up and started to leave the table.

'Stay there, Jonathan,' Dad said icily. 'Don't you leave your place.'

'You bitch, Nicola!' Sally snarled at me. 'You rotten bitch!'

Mum glared at Sally and said, 'Don't speak like that, Sally.'

'Why shouldn't I? Everything she does is aimed at causing trouble and drawing attention to herself.' Then she turned to me. 'I've really had it with you, Nicola. I really have! You're spoiling everybody's holiday!'

I was about to tell her what I thought of her, when Dad hissed at me, 'Don't say one more word, Nicola, or I'll knock you from here to kingdom come. I've had enough too.'

We finished the meal in almost total silence.

It was a disastrous holiday – the last we ever took together as a family. When we returned home, we found there was even more tension between us than there had been before we left.

# CHAPTER NINE

## *Psychiatric Care*

After the holiday in Majorca, I felt I was being treated as a prisoner at home. Mum constantly kept an eye on me and, whenever I suggested it would be best for me to live on my own, Dad would say that, until I'd sorted myself out, I wasn't capable of looking after myself.

I continued to experience times when I felt a total revulsion with myself and then I became so self-obsessed that I couldn't even talk to anybody else. On one such night, a week or so after we'd returned from Majorca, my parents were so concerned about me that Dad told me I had to sleep with my mother and he would use the bed in my room. I refused, but he insisted.

After Mum had gone to sleep, I sneaked silently out of her bed and went into the bathroom. After I'd locked the door and switched on the light, I stared at my face in the mirror. I could stand it no longer. Taking one of Dad's razor-blades, I slashed into the horrible face I hated so much. Then, with the blood seeping out of the fine cuts, I went back and lay next to Mum in bed.

I was awakened in the morning by a loud bellow and Dad hitting me with one hell of a wallop. Having brought a tray of tea into the room, he'd seen the blood-stained pillow and had gone berserk. Mum, who'd also been fast asleep, was throwing herself all over me to stop him hitting me any more as he screamed, 'You sodding rotten bitch! What the bloody hell have you done now?'

'Ed, go and phone the doctor,' Mum commanded.

'I'll kill her. That's it! I've had all I can bloody well take of that girl!'

'Stop it, Ed! Phone Dr Sangster. Tell him he's got to do something now.'

'Somebody better do something. I'm not taking any more of this crap. The girl needs a bloody great kick up the arse and I'll tell you this – I can't hold on for much longer. She's damn well going to get it! Look at her face! Look at this blood!'

'Ed, stop shouting and phone the doctor.'

Still furious, Dad stormed out of the room.

I'd cleaned myself up, got dressed and put on my wig by the time Dr Sangster arrived, but with my slashed face and sun-blistered chest I was still in quite a state. Seeing my parents and me together, he must have been shocked by the obvious tension that existed between us.

'I think the best thing for everyone,' he said, 'is for me to take Nicola back into hospital to give you a break. Now, Nicola, do you want your mother to bring you in or will you come back with me?'

I thought, There's no way I'm going anywhere with my mother, and so I said sweetly, 'I'll come with you, doctor.'

I packed my night-wear in the little case my parents had bought me for my dancing things and then I gaily went off with the doctor in his lovely open-topped sports car. If nothing else, I had at least managed to get away from home.

At the hospital, I was given cream for my badly blistered chest and for the cuts on my face, which apparently weren't deep enough to need stitches. I was then taken to a side ward and told to change into my night-dress. Presumably because they felt they had to keep an eye on me, they left me only with my dressing-gown and slippers – the clothes I had been wearing were taken away. Suspecting this might happen, I'd taken the precaution of transferring the loose change from my coat to my dressing-gown.

After I'd climbed into the hospital bed, Dr Sangster arrived and gave me a long lecture about the way he expected me to behave. Then I was left alone.

I'm not going to stay here, I thought. There's nothing wrong with me. I'm not ill. I'm going to run away.

When everything seemed quiet, I got up, put on my dressing-gown and slippers, and just walked out of the hospital. I went to the nearest telephone box and called a cab. When it pulled up, I said to the driver, 'I'm just off to a pyjama party!'

The cab took me to the home of my friend, Peter Kotting. I trusted him because, unlike all the other men I'd met, he never tried to pressure me into having a physical relationship.

Peter's parents were out when I arrived and he was having a drink in the kitchen with a few friends. They all thought it was a great hoot that I'd turned up in my night-clothes. None of them would believe I was actually supposed to be in hospital. So I showed them the plastic identity tab round my wrist.

'I think I'd better phone your parents,' Peter said.

I grabbed a kitchen knife and jabbed it towards him. 'Peter, don't you dare phone my parents,' I snarled. 'Don't you dare tell anybody I'm here!'

I ran into the downstairs toilet and locked the door. Some time later, a policeman arrived and coaxed me to unlock the door and put down the knife. Eventually, I did and was driven back to the hospital.

Dr Sangster was waiting for me and gave me a dressing down. 'Now look here, young lady. When I pull the strings, you bloody well dance. I'm not having you doing things like this and so I'm going to discipline you. I'm taking away your dressing-gown and slippers. I've alerted the hospital security. So don't think there's any chance of your getting away again. From now on, you do as I tell you.'

Nicola was kept in hospital for ten days. She was allowed home so she could go with the rest of her family to the first group therapy session at the adolescent unit of the psychiatric hospital.

Nobody was looking forward to it.

The idea of parents and children being interviewed together certainly didn't appeal to Ed. As he saw it, democracy in government was one thing – within a family, it was nothing more than a load of impractical rubbish. Children could have their say but, if he disagreed with them, that was the end of it. It was the duty of a father to be determined and decisive.

Pam had her own reasons for being reluctant to have all the issues raised in front of her children. Already close to breaking-point, she had become convinced that she was to blame for Nicola's behaviour. Friends had often said to her, 'What did you do differently with Nicola than you did with the other two?' She too wondered. Perhaps I shouldn't have shouted at her that day, she thought. Was she brain-damaged as a baby when I tripped and she knocked her head on the station steps? She analysed everything and concluded that it was because she'd once had an affair that Nicola was ill. Somehow, Nicola must have found out what was happening and, as a result, had been psychologically damaged. Both Sally and Johnnie were sure the group therapy session would be a waste of time.

Johnnie didn't want the embarrassment or inconvenience of taking time off school to visit a psychiatric hospital. As Nicola had begun to show less interest in him and the rest of the family, he had tended to cease thinking of her as a sister. By this time, he felt she meant nothing to him. He hated it when at weekends or during the holidays he was at home and she came into the room – fat and shaven-headed, with a strange look in her eyes. She'd had so much and thrown it all away.

Sally too was fed up with her sister. Having just fallen seriously in love for the first time, Sally felt she needed her parents' support, but they didn't have the energy left to deal with her problems. They were preoccupied with Nicola, who once again was stealing all their attention.

The group therapy session turned out to be even worse than any of them had feared.

At the beginning, they were all told the aim of the session was to rebuild communications in a family where they'd broken down and so they mustn't hold anything back. Every issue and personal grievance should be discussed in front of the whole family.

Nicola said, 'I can't say the things I want to in front of my family.'

'It doesn't matter,' one of the two psychiatrists present replied. 'You've got to learn to say them and until you do learn to say them, you must keep quiet about them.'

Everybody was temporarily silenced by that. Rebuffed, Nicola decided at that point she was going to take no further part in the session.

Pam tried asking a question: 'Nicola's told me she had three periods in one month. Do you think that's important?'

The psychiatrist leaned back in his chair as though he was about to say something of earth-shattering importance. 'Do you?' he sonorously asked.

Pam and Ed looked at each other in astonishment.

Eventually, they did begin to talk and the session soon seemed in danger of degenerating into an opportunity for everyone to vent their anger and frustration. Every member of the family came under attack, apart from Nicola.

Feeling that this was leading nowhere and desperately hoping that something might come out of the session to help her daughter, Pam decided to be open and honest as she'd been asked to be. Deeply upset, she began to talk about the affair she'd had when Nicola was eleven. Ed was furious with his wife and tried to stop her continuing. Nicola feigned shock and grief.

'Oh, my poor dad,' she groaned.

Ed was having none of his daughter's assumed sympathy. 'Your mother was a fool to have said that,' he snapped at her. 'And I'll tell you something else, I haven't been innocent all my life but I wouldn't tell you what I've done and what I haven't done.'

By the time the session ended, the tensions within the Owen family had substantially increased.

Convinced now that she had just cause, Nicola's hatred for her mother was unconcealed. Pam lived in constant fear not only that her daughter might do something terrible at any time but that she would fly into such a rage she'd be physically violent.

\*     \*     \*

One afternoon, I was in my room, supposed to be doing my ironing. Mum came in and found me lying on the bed.

'I'm just going down to the shops,' she said. 'I want you to come with me.'

'No way,' I said. 'What I'm going to do is my ironing.'

'No you won't. I've got to go out and I'm not going to leave you alone in the house.'

'Well, that's what you'll have to do, because I'm not going with you.'

Mum just stood there. I got so wound up because she obviously wasn't going to give in that I jumped up, grabbed the iron and chased her round the house. Only the intervention of Mrs Green, the daily help, stopped me seriously hurting Mum.

The anger I felt towards her increased my determination to leave home, but Dad would have none of it. He wouldn't even agree that I could take a bed-sit or at least stay with a relative during the week when I went to the Arts

Education School. So when I started there, I had to travel to London each day by train.

Even on the first day of term, I knew I was going to have problems. I was still wearing my wig, was very overweight and didn't feel at all right within myself. There were a lot of talented people there and everything was totally new to me. I suddenly felt completely out of my depth. I didn't even like mixing with the other students.

At the end of the first week, I decided I wasn't going to go back any more. On the Monday morning of the second week, I pretended to set off and then went to hide in Sally's wardrobe. I didn't come out until everybody else had left the house. Mum and Dad were now at the end of their tether and I knew it would take only a little push for them to say I could leave home. Later that afternoon, I switched on the iron and left it face down on the ironing board so it would scorch the cover. Then I poured cooking oil all over my bed. As soon as Sally returned from school, I told her what I'd done and went off to a friend's house.

It was a terrible shock for both Mum and Dad when they heard I had no intention of returning to the Arts Education School. Their little Nicola wasn't going to be a dancing star any more. It was the end of their dream. Mum didn't find it easy to accept. When she was a girl, she'd wanted to go to art school but, instead, had to become a secretary. So it was as though the door to a more creative life had been slammed on her for the second time. But I wasn't going to be intimidated. 'The only thing I want to do is to leave home,' I said.

A few days later, we had our second group therapy session at the adolescent unit. I told the psychiatrists that I wouldn't get better until I'd left home. I desperately wanted to be independent, but Dad wouldn't let me go.

One of them said, 'I agree. The best thing for you to do, Nicola, is to leave home. You need to get away from the tension.' He then turned to Dad and asked, 'What do you think about that, Mr Owen?'

'Of course she can leave home,' he replied unexpectedly. 'If she doesn't, I'm sure I'll end up killing her!'

I was astonished. At last, I could leave home.

But before I did, I had one final spiteful act to perform. Sally had become extremely offhand with me. We were no longer the good friends we once had been. I'd always been jealous of her because she had no difficulty in finding boyfriends, whereas I seemed incapable of forming any relationship. Now that she was madly in love with this boy called Roy, I was incensed. Stupidly, she'd told me she was taking birth-control pills, which she kept hidden in a hole she'd made in a book. She was only fifteen and, of course, my parents were unaware of what was going on. I knew that Dad would go berserk if he found out. I'd no intention of telling him directly. So, instead, I told Mrs Green, sure that she'd think it was her duty to tell my parents.

I went first to live with my Auntie Mo and then, three weeks later, to a shared flat in Tottenham, which was a long way from home. Mum and Dad helped me move in, buying me a beautiful duvet, cover and matching pillowcases, some saucepans and other cooking utensils.

I found a job as an interviewer for an employment agency and was at first very successful, so much so that on the training course I was awarded a bottle of champagne as the person who showed the greatest potential. I was very surprised, because I really didn't have any confidence. I didn't even think anybody had noticed me.

Receiving a weekly pay cheque was enjoyable, but I still had an uncontrollable desire to eat and so, after I'd paid the rent, everything I earned went on food. At night, I'd return to the flat and see Sandra, the girl I was sharing with, going out with a succession of different boyfriends. One day, Sandra said she was getting an evening job in a pub and that I could also work there. So both of us became barmaids in a seedy pub to get extra cash. It was rather unpleasant there, but it was the only form of social life I had outside work.

I kept in touch with Mum and Dad by phone. They told me their news and I gave them a pack of lies about how happy I was, the parties I'd been to and the handsome men that desperately wanted to marry me.

*     *     *

With Nicola, their problem daughter, having just left home, it was all too easy for Ed and Pam to over-react and not be as sensitive as they might have been when they heard from Mrs Green that Sally was on the pill.

Ed immediately rang the parents of Roy, Sally's eighteen-year-old boyfriend. 'Your son's consorting with my daughter and she's under age,' he said. 'What are you going to do about it?'

'Come on, Mr Owen. You were young once yourself!'

That was not the reply most likely to pacify Ed! 'How would you react if it was your daughter?' he demanded angrily.

'I agree with you. I wouldn't like it. But what can you expect me to do about it?'

Ed banned Sally from ever seeing her boyfriend again.

But, being a determined and independent young woman who was in love, Sally took no notice. One day when Ed was away on business, she said to her mother, 'If you don't give me permission to see Roy, I'm going to leave home. Roy's going to buy me a piano and we're going to have a car and we're going to live together.'

Faced with this ultimatum from her fifteen-year-old daughter, Pam said, 'I think I'd better have a word with you and Roy. You can't bring him to the house because I'm not going against what your dad has said. So I'll meet you both in Sidcup and we can talk things over.'

The meeting was a disaster. Sally and Roy were adamant and Pam just couldn't get through to them. She was so infuriated and upset by the time she arrived back home that she rang the police.

'Go carefully, Mrs Owen,' the policeman said. 'She might leave home. It happens all the time.'

There was something about his tone that made Pam feel that the policeman knew about Nicola and so was suspicious that it was the home environment and the parents who were creating the problems for their teenage daughters. Upset by this, Pam said, 'But he's over eighteen and he's having an affair with my daughter who's under age. You must be able to do something about that.'

'We can't just go round and have a word with the boy,' the policeman replied, 'because then he could accuse us of harassment.'

'Well, my husband and I can take him to court.'

'I don't advise that, madam. You've no idea how horrible it can be for the girl and her parents when everything comes out in court.'

This incensed Pam. She was so furious with Sally for causing new worries when there were worries enough to be going on with that, when her daughter eventually came home, Pam had an almighty row with her.

The next night, Ed came home and Pam told him what had happened.

'Right then,' Ed said and strode to the bottom of the stairs. 'Sally!' he shouted.

'Yes,' she answered.

'Pack your bags! If Roy wants the privileges of marriage, there's no need for him to wait until February when you're sixteen. He can have you and the responsibility of you now.'

Down came Sally with her bags packed, assuming that she was going to be welcomed by Roy with open arms.

Ed drove her round to Roy's house and put Sally and her bags on his doorstep.

Roy's father came rushing out. 'What's all this about, Mr Owen?' he demanded.

'It's very simple. You said you can't do anything about

111

your son. If that's the case, let your son take responsibility. I'm not having my daughter living at home while she continues to see your son. So I've brought her here and now you have a potential daughter-in-law!'

The boy's father didn't know what to say at first, but he eventually agreed to let Sally sleep on the settee that night. 'But, after that, you can't stay here,' he told her.

The next morning, Sally and Roy went to Nicola's flat in Tottenham to ask if they could stay there.

'I can barely cope with looking after myself,' Nicola said. 'I certainly can't cope with looking after you two.'

That night, it was pouring with rain when Ed heard a knock at the front door and went to open it.

Sally was standing there. 'Dad! You've got to take responsibility for me,' she announced pertly. 'I'm only fifteen!'

'Sally!' he replied. 'All the time you're consorting with that Roy, he can have the worry of you.' With that, he put her in the car and whisked her back to Roy's house.

Roy's father came out, shaking his fist. But Ed drove back home where Pam was hunched up in an armchair, weeping.

The next morning, still extremely upset, Pam was making breakfast as Lizzie, the Dalmatian, went out into the garden. She did not return when Pam called. Concerned, Pam went outside and found Lizzie lying, unable to move, on the garden terrace.

Pam immediately telephoned Paul Ashburner, a neighbour who was a partner in a local veterinary practice. A handsome, bearded man in his late thirties, he came immediately.

'It's her nervous system that's gone, I'm afraid,' he said. After Lizzie had been given an injection, she was carried back into the kitchen. 'Let's give it a couple of hours,' he said. 'If she responds to this, then maybe there's a chance.'

Pam cuddled Lizzie for a while and, after the two hours had passed, Paul Ashburner returned. By this time, Pam's parents had arrived and as they and Pam watched tearfully, Ed and Paul lifted Lizzie out of her basket and on to her feet. The beautiful Dalmatian that had been a family companion for fourteen years stood on the kitchen floor as still as a marble statue.

'Is there nothing else we can do, Paul?' Ed asked.

' 'Fraid not.'

'It's the end for her then?'

Paul slowly nodded.

Ed lifted the dog back into her basket and cradled her in his arms as Paul took a syringe from his bag.

Pam ran into the sitting-room and sobbed. It seemed to her as if everything she loved was being taken away from her.

As Ed spoke comfortingly to Lizzie, Paul Ashburner gave her the final injection.

Wrapped in a red dressing-gown that Nicola had worn as a child, Lizzie was buried by Ed and Pam's father at the bottom of the garden between two rose bushes.

While this was being done, Pam's mother rang Roy's father and said, 'There's such a lot of unhappiness in this house at the moment. My daughter's all distraught. Nicola's left home, the dog has just died and there's all this trouble with Sally. Isn't there anything you can do?'

'All right,' he replied. 'I'll have a word with Roy.'

In the early evening, Sally and Roy arrived, both in tears.

'We've agreed,' Sally sobbed, 'that we won't see each other any more.'

Pam held out her arms to her daughter and, both weeping, they cuddled each other.

Even Ed was moved and, as the young man shuffled off on his own, said, 'Goodbye, Roy, and thank you.'

After Pam's parents had left and Sally had gone up to bed, Ed and Pam sat together in silence. Both were deeply upset by the day's events and through both their minds ran the firm conviction that, for reasons they could not fathom, they were proving to be disastrous failures as parents.

★      ★      ★

113

I was anything but happy living in London. I couldn't concentrate for any length of time on anything and I soon grew bored with my job. I started making false records and telling people I'd found them work when I hadn't. It was obvious I'd get caught, but once again it was as though I wanted to get myself into trouble.

Early in November, I was called in by the manager, who said, 'I can either sack you or you can resign – either way you've got to go.'

'What's the difference?'

'If we sack you, we don't give you a reference but we give you a month's money. If you resign, you get no money but we'll give you a reference.'

'That's it,' I said. 'Sack me.'

I left there and then blew the month's money on food which I ate in a couple of days. That left my work in the pub as my only source of income. Fortunately, I soon found another job. Unfortunately, it was the worst thing I could have done. I was employed as a booker in a modelling agency. Every day, I was dealing with stunning girls who had real style. They were just as I'd been a few years earlier. But I'd become grossly overweight, wore baggy black clothes, and was still wearing my blessed wig.

As soon as I started the job, I began to drink heavily. Every time I had a coffee, I'd lace it with a large sherry. Apparently, I was rude to the models and none of them liked me. After six weeks, I was sacked.

It was almost Christmas and Sandra had gone away for a few days. I gorged all her food and then, knowing I couldn't control myself any more, I rang home. When Mum answered, I said, 'Can you come and fetch me, Mum? Please just come and fetch me. I don't want to live here any more.'

'I will,' Mum said, 'but we can't be the way we were. You'll have to go out to work. We're not having this lying in bed all day. It's all so depressing.'

Mum and Dad came to collect me. They settled up all my debts, loaded my belongings into the car, and drove me home. The only thing that made me feel pleased to be there was being welcomed by Emma, the five-week-old border collie puppy that Mum had just acquired to replace poor Lizzie.

After only three months of independence, I was back to square one. With no job, no flat of my own and no prospects, I was once again living at home with Mum and Dad.

# CHAPTER TEN

## *Destruction*

I felt totally ashamed. There was nothing to feel proud of. My parents had very high ideals and, instead of being wonderful in their eyes, I'd become terrible. It wasn't as though my parents were the kind of people who would say, 'It doesn't matter. You can do whatever you want to do.' I felt that my parents wanted me to be the best and I was a failure.

There was also my dramatic physical change. It wasn't just that I'd shaved off my hair and that I was extremely bloated. My eyes had a permanent glazed look about them as if they were made of glass. People found it eerie to look at me. It was as though I had no feeling, no life. The will to live had gone and I didn't care.

All I wanted to do was to sleep all day, but my parents insisted that I should find another job. I couldn't face the pressure they were putting on me and so I'd wander the streets just wishing I could be in bed.

I couldn't talk to either of my parents. Every time they said I should get a job, tidy my room, stop taking food, eat less, get out of bed or generally pull myself together, something inside me snapped and I'd bellow at them to leave me alone. There were endless scenes. One day towards the end of January, I flew into a rage, smashed up my bedroom and ran off into the woods wearing my dressing-gown and slippers.

Things had become so bad at home that Mum phoned

the adolescent unit of the psychiatric hospital to ask for immediate help and was told the earliest appointment she could have was in a fortnight's time. It was an appointment that came too late.

Three days after Mum's call to the hospital, I had a blazing row with my father who was demanding that I should start making a useful contribution to the family. The following day, I ran away in the pouring rain to Brighton.

As I had no money, I got on the train without a ticket. When I arrived in Brighton I was caught by the railway police but, after I'd given them a false name and address, they let me go. I then went to stay in the same grotty boarding-house as I had when I'd run away from home seven months before.

The same Italian was working at the reception desk. 'Haven't you stayed here before?' he asked.

I was so embarrassed by the amount of weight I'd put on that I said, 'No, never. You must be thinking of my sister, Kelly. She stayed here last summer.'

'You're very similar,' he said. 'Your sister's really attractive. What's she doing now?'

There was a perverse delight in being the fat, ugly sister and hearing him talk about how attractive I'd been. I also noticed that this time he didn't make the slightest effort to chat me up.

I was given the same room as before, although I had no idea how I was going to pay the bill at the end of my stay. That afternoon, I walked around, arriving back at the boarding-house soaking wet. In the evening, I went downstairs to dinner and ordered a bottle of wine.

During the course of the meal, two seedy-looking middle-aged men came across to my table. They said they were jewellery salesmen and asked if I'd like them to show me the sights of the town. As I'd nothing better to do, I went with them on what turned out to be a prolonged pub-crawl. In each pub, they ordered champagne and I became drunker and drunker. At one stage, they presented me with a diamond ring. I said I didn't want it, but they insisted it was one of their samples and cost them nothing.

By the time we reached the seventh pub, I was swaying all over the place and my two companions were propping me up to make sure I didn't fall down. The publican came across to us and barked at me, 'Get out of my pub. We don't want whores like you in this pub. Get out!'

Even with my befuddled brain, I knew what he was saying. Why did he say that? I wasn't a whore. I was still a virgin. I'd never sexually misbehaved in my life. So why did he think I was a whore?

I burst into tears and ran blindly out of the pub. I kept on running until I collapsed in the doorway of a Burton's shop. I crouched there in the corner, sobbing. Suddenly, I felt a tap on my shoulder. A young man in his mid-twenties was standing there, asking me if he could help.

We talked for a while. I told him something of what had happened and that I'd run away from home. He said he was a student who'd come from South Africa to study in Brighton.

'It's cold and wet here,' he said. 'Why don't we go back to my place and have a coffee? At least it's warm there and we can finish telling each other our life stories in comfort.'

He'd shown me such kindness that I went with him. But instead of giving me coffee, he gave me more and more wine. Then he seduced me. I remember him pulling off my clothes. I remember him pushing my knees up to my chest. I remember him taking my virginity. All the time, I was crying. I hated what he was doing. I hated the way he'd been pawing me. I hated this ugly, odious man. Above all, I hated myself.

I knew then that I'd lost everything. I was seventeen years old and yet my looks, my figure, my pretty hair, my dancing career, my determination, my enthusiasm for life had already gone. Now, in the seediest most degrading way possible, I'd lost the last thing that remained – my virginity.

The next morning, I got up and shuffled into the communal bathroom. In the cracked mirror, I stared at my red, blotchy face and felt nauseous as I recalled what had happened. Dad had been so eloquent about how special love-making should be. I'd always had a fantasy about falling in love with a handsome man who'd worship at my feet and who, as a virgin dressed in white, I'd marry. Now, it wasn't to be. Instead of living happily ever after, I no longer wanted to live at all.

On my way out, the landlady stared at me as though I was the lowest of the low. I made my way back to the boarding-house. I felt totally numb. I ran a bath and just lay there. What I couldn't comprehend was why I was determined to destroy myself. I was so alone. I couldn't explain my feelings to anyone and especially not to Dad. I couldn't even explain them to myself.

I was then faced with the problem of how I was going to pay my bill. I wandered the streets for ages. When I thought my sister would be alone in the house, I phoned home from a call-box. After Sally had enquired if I was all right, she suggested that she rang Nanny, who lived in Hastings, to ask her if she'd come and pick me up. It was only much later that I discovered Mum had been at home, listening to my call on the other phone and passing written messages to Sally who then relayed them on to me.

Nan and Grandad came dashing down to Brighton, paid the hotel bill for me, and took me back to their bungalow, where I had another bath. I couldn't tell them what had happened and so they'd no idea why I was so distressed. Poor Nan and Grandad didn't know what to say to me.

'What am I going to do?' I sobbed.

'But you're a big girl anyway, Nicola,' Grandad said, thinking I was worried about being overweight. 'You're big boned.'

'But I'm not!'

After I'd had a hot meal, Grandad took me to the station and bought me the ticket home. The only thing Mum said to me when she opened the door was, 'Hello, Nick. Have you enjoyed your holiday?' I smiled, nodded and went straight up to my room.

That Friday evening, my parents brought Johnnie home from his boarding-school for the weekend. They'd promised to take him to the cinema and so it was agreed that Sally and I would stay at home together.

After my parents had driven off with Johnnie, I asked Sally to come with me to buy a bottle of sherry at the off-licence. As we were walking through the woods, I told her what had happened. I felt I needed to talk to somebody about having been robbed of my virginity. Not knowing the best way to tell her or how she'd respond, I was giggling as I spoke. It was as if I was trying to pretend that I didn't care.

'You're lying again,' Sally said.

'I'm not. There's no reason to lie.'

'You don't need a reason. You're always lying and I don't believe you.'

'When have I ever lied to you?'

'All the time – about stealing food, your drinking, being raped. It's all lies. And what about the time you told me you'd got cancer and were going to die? You reduced me to tears and then said it was all a joke.'

'But I'm not lying now,' I protested feebly. I knew it was to no avail. There was an insurmountable barrier between us.

We went back home, played some music, drank a glass of sherry and I went to bed. I just wanted to sleep and sleep and sleep. I felt as though I had nothing to live for. Where were my dancing skills now, my parents' respect, my parents' love, my friends, my boyfriends, my sister? I was alone with nothing. I was weird, I was unbalanced, I was sick and I couldn't cope with it any more.

The next morning, Dad came breezing into my room and said, 'Right, Nicola. Get yourself up. It's seven-fifteen already and the day's almost over.' I opened my eyes, but didn't stir. 'Show a leg, Nicola,' he went on. 'We're taking you up to London with us. We've got to take Sally to the Royal Academy and we're dropping Johnnie off at Skate City. Come on, Nicola!'

'I'm not coming. I'm staying here.'

'No, you're not! Mum thinks she'll buy you a new dress and we'll have coffee in that little French pâtisserie in Marylebone High Street. So up you get.'

'I don't want to go, Dad. I'm too tired.'

'Don't be ridiculous. You'll be fine once we're all in London.'

'Look, Dad, I don't want to go. Just leave me alone, will you?'

'You're coming with us, Nicola!' he said determinedly.

'I don't want to go. Leave me alone!' I snapped back.

Incensed by my tone and refusal to budge, Dad began to lose his temper. 'Like hell, Nicola! I'm not leaving you alone in this house so you can eat your way though the whole of this family's weekend food!'

'I won't eat your bloody food,' I protested loudly. 'I just want to be left alone. I'm tired, Dad. Don't you understand? I'm not coming.'

'All right, so don't come. But I'm not having you in this house. You'll have to go over and see Nannie Owen at Sidcup. The walk will do you good. And I want your house key,' he snapped and with that, he walked across to the dressing-table and prized the key off my key-ring. 'Now get out of that bed. We'll be leaving in forty minutes and I want you out of the house by then.'

I didn't want to see Nannie Owen. It was a cold February day and all I wanted to do was to stay in my warm bedroom. 'Why can't you leave me alone?' I screamed at Dad as he was walking out.

He turned and shouted back at me. 'You're bloody useless, Nicola! Why don't you pull yourself together and start contributing to the family? Now, for the last time, get out of that bed!'

He slammed the door and I began to cry. But I got dressed and, as I left my room, Sally hurried up to me. Without saying a word, she slipped something into my hand. As she rushed away, I looked down at what she'd given me. It was her front-door key.

We all left the house together. Johnnie was with his skateboard, eager to get off. Mum and Dad jumped into the car and Sally gave me a tiny wave. As they drove off, I trudged down the road. It had begun to drizzle.

Once the car was out of sight, I quickly returned home. As soon as I put the key into the door, I felt a burst of adrenalin, a real sense of pleasure at doing something my parents didn't even dream I was doing.

I headed straight into the kitchen. As Dad had said I would, I started to work my way through the food in the larder. I ate a family-sized harvest pie with a tin of custard, a salad bowl full of breakfast cereal, several cakes and a dozen slices of toast and jam. I just couldn't believe the amount I was capable of eating. By the time I'd finished, my stomach was like a fully inflated balloon.

Then I walked into the dining-room, opened my father's drinks cabinet and proceeded to knock back half a bottle of whisky as though it was beer. Next I finished off the sherry I'd bought with Sally the previous evening.

As I climbed the stairs, I was laughing. There's no hope for you any more, I thought. You're mad. You're evil. You're sick and I don't care about you. I'm not going to fight for you any more.

In Sally's room, I put a record on her expensive music centre, turned up the volume and swayed about drunkenly – a repulsive, obese woman dancing, imagining myself to be the girl I once was. Suddenly catching sight of myself in her mirror, I stopped, switched off the record and walked into my bedroom.

I stared out of the window. It was a grey, cheerless February day. The drizzle rattled warningly against the window panes and, with a low whisper, a cold wind gusted through the conifers. The barren garden was dominated by a giant weeping willow, standing lethargic and isolated in the middle of the sodden lawn. The starkness of the scene was relieved only by the evergreens around the borders of the garden. I could remember the day they were planted. It seemed so long ago. Nearer to me, the rose bushes were lifeless and cold. Only a few months ago, they had been a spectacular mass of vivid colour.

I turned away and walked over to the full-length mirror on my bedroom wall. I no longer knew the girl staring back at me. I felt my throat tightening, but I couldn't cry . . .

# CHAPTER ELEVEN

## *Arrest*

. . . There was the acrid smell and fierce crackling roar of burning. As I looked up the stairs, swirling black smoke was ominously edging its way downwards.

It had to be a terrifying nightmare. Any second, I'd wake up and everything would be as it always was.

Suddenly, I became aware of the doorbell's persistent ringing. Automatically, I got up and opened the front door. As I did so, I heard the distant sounds of sirens and clashing bells rapidly coming closer.

Somebody hoisted me out of the house. There was thick, billowing smoke everywhere. Emma jumped out of my arms and scampered into the small crowd that was standing outside the burning house.

A neighbour grabbed hold of me so firmly that her nails dug into my hand. 'You did it, Nicola,' she hissed, 'didn't you? You set fire to the house!'

She dragged me down to her house, gave me a brandy and made me lie on a bed. I was willing myself to be far away from this world. If you concentrate hard enough, I told myself, you won't be here.

But it didn't happen. I could still hear the commotion of clanging bells and roaring engines going on up the road.

The neighbour brought a fireman into the room where I was lying. 'Did you do it?' he demanded.

'Yes,' I replied.

\*     \*     \*

It had been a dispiriting morning for Ed and Pam. Their efforts to recreate past pleasures of family outings to the West End had failed abysmally. So they were relieved when it was time to collect Sally from the Royal Academy.

As Pam waited in the car, Ed walked up the steps and on through the large main doors. A few minutes later, she saw him returning with Sally. They were half-way down the steps, when a woman ran out of the building.

'Mr Owen,' she called.

Turning quickly round, Ed said, 'Yes. That's me.'

'There's an urgent telephone call for you.'

Concerned that he was about to hear bad news, he bounded up the steps and followed the woman into an office, where she pointed to the telephone receiver lying on top of the highly polished, antique table.

'Ed Owen speaking,' he said.

'Ed. It's Gerald.'

This friend and neighbour was the Secretary of the London Fire Brigade. When he heard his voice, Ed knew his worst fears were about to be confirmed. 'Yes,' he said anxiously.

'You've had a fire in the house.'

There could be only one cause. 'Is Nicola all right?' he demanded anxiously.

'Yes, she's OK. And so's the puppy,' Gerald said, giving Ed the name of the neighbour who had taken them both in.

'Nicola's not hurt in any way? You're sure?'

'Absolutely sure. She's quite all right, Ed.'

'And how bad's the fire, Gerald?'

'Well, not too bad.'

Ed sensed the lack of conviction in the answer. 'Not too bad you say?' he asked searchingly.

There was a pause before Gerald quietly replied, 'No. It's pretty bad I'm afraid.'

'I'll be there in about fifty minutes,' Ed said. 'And thank you, Gerald.'

He rushed out of the office and down the stairs to the car. 'She's set fire to the house!' he announced. 'But she's all right and so's Emma.'

Pam slumped down in the seat and moaned in despair.

Sally burst into tears and between her sobs shouted, 'Oh, the bitch, the bitch. What has she done to our lovely home? I'll never forgive her, never.' As Ed drove off, she lapsed into subdued sobbing. They had nearly reached Skate City, before she broke the tense silence by blurting out in a high-pitched wail, 'I gave her my key. Please forgive me.'

Already mentally flailed by his anxiety and distress, Ed was about to respond angrily, but Pam looked at him and said quietly, 'Don't, Ed. Even if she hadn't been given the key, Nicola would have found some way of getting back into the house.'

At Skate City, Johnnie was excitedly awaiting his parents' arrival, desperate to show them the red proficiency badge he'd been awarded after his morning's hard work. He ran to the car and gleefully began, 'Look, Dad. I've got . . .'

'Get in the car, son,' Ed said. 'There's no time for that. Nicola's burnt the house down.'

Bemused and upset, Johnnie joined his sister in the back of the car. As she'd always done with her dancing, Nicola had once again managed to top his own achievement, but this time in the most dreadful of ways. His parents could hardly be expected to take any interest in his little red badge when his elder sister had apparently just destroyed the family home.

As they drove into Camden Road, they immediately saw the fire engine, standing like a sentinel in front of their house. But before they reached it, Ed stopped the car outside the house of the neighbours who were looking after Nicola. Pam's priority was to see her daughter and, without even glancing up the road, she quickly left the car.

Accompanied by his two younger children, Ed cautiously drove the short distance towards their home, the fire engine growing ever larger as they approached. As he brought the car to a halt beside it, Ed glanced at the exhausted, smoke-blackened firemen sprawled over the appliance like battle-worn soldiers awaiting further orders.

It was only after he had clambered out of the car that he dared look at the house. Immediately, he felt relieved. From the front, the house looked intact and there was no discernible damage. The only noticeable difference was that all the windows were black-tinted, as though they belonged to an expensive sports coupé or a foreign diplomat's stretched limousine.

'Mr Owen?'

Ed turned to look at the solemn-faced chief fireman. 'That's me,' he responded.

'I'll show you over the house, sir.'

'Thank you.'

The two men crossed the front lawn and entered the house. Unnoticed, Johnnie and Sally followed closely behind.

Inside, there was the all-pervading, unpleasantly pungent smell of a dead fire which was to linger for months, long after all the repairs and redecorations had been completed. Underfoot, the waterlogged carpets squelched. Ed looked up to the upper hall. Everything up there was black, as though some maniac had sprayed the place with gallons of liquid tar.

'The fire started in the bedroom above the kitchen,' the chief fireman stated as calmly as if reading a weather forecast. 'I understand it was your eldest daughter's room.'

Ed, drained of all emotion, could only nod.

The chief fireman opened the kitchen door. There was no ceiling, nor was there a bedroom above it. There was a gaping hole in the roof so that, through the fire-damaged rafters, Ed could see the grey sky above. High up, to one side of the void, the cold-water tank hung at a crazy angle, still dripping water from a fractured pipe on to the layer of charred black debris that was littering the once immaculate kitchen floor.

'I'll show you upstairs, sir, but be careful. Some of the landing has been burnt away.'

Ed silently followed the chief fireman upstairs. There was no longer an airing cupboard or Nicola's bedroom – just blackened brickwork. Only a few charred flooring joists remained in that area of the upper hall.

'I have to ask, sir, if you had some sort of chemical stored in the loft.'

'No,' Ed mumbled. 'Why do you ask?'

'Because the fire was of such intense heat. It was most unusual for a fire in a domestic property. The buildup of gases was so rapid that we had to break open the roof over the next bedroom to release them before the house exploded. Another minute and you would have lost everything.'

'I don't understand, officer.'

'The fire was so intense it looked as though it was fuelled by either petrol or some chemical. It took hold very rapidly and went through most of the loft, setting alight the roofing felt. The melted bitumen and the smoke had scorched and blackened the rest of the house that the flames didn't reach.'

Ed nodded. It was difficult for him to take in what was being said. What he saw told him everything. He was standing in the blackened ruin of what had been, only a few hours before, the beautiful home that he and his wife had worked so hard to provide for their family.

'We had to throw out the burning contents of the loft on to the garden and douse them out there,' the chief fireman continued to report. 'Funnily enough, there's a heavy wooden trunk still up in the loft that appears to have survived unscathed.'

While Ed was being shown the rest of the damage, Sally and Johnnie wandered around on their own, viewing the destruction. Holding her breath as she tiptoed to the chasm that had once been her sister's bedroom, Sally returned to her own room. Everything visible was smoke-blackened. Pulling open the top drawer of the blackened hulk that had once been a white chest of drawers, she discovered that her underwear, which earlier in the day had been crisply clean and smelling of lavender, looked and smelt like black, oily rags. As she lifted up the last layer, she was amazed to see that even the bottom of the drawer was as black as everything else in the room.

'Come and look at my room, Sally.' Johnnie, obviously deeply upset, was standing in the doorway.

She followed him to his bedroom which that morning had been festooned with model aircraft made from plastic kits – Second World War bombers, modern jet fighters and airliners. The wires that once had suspended them at different heights and angles were still there but, instead of aircraft hanging at the ends, there were only shapeless, black, molten blobs.

'I'm so sorry, Johnnie,' Sally said, curling her arm around his shoulder.

Close to tears, he said, more to himself than his sister, 'Everything I've ever done, that Nicola has taken away from me.'

'But your fish are still all right, Johnnie. Look!' Sally exclaimed, pointing to the fish tank where, despite the thick layer of black debris on the lid of the tank, the tropical fish were still swimming around.

But Johnnie was not to be consoled. He rushed off and sought sanctuary in the downstairs toilet which, unlike the rest of the house, was surprisingly clean. Having locked the door, he sat there and sobbed.

Sally went downstairs to look for her father. By the time she found him, the chief fireman had left. Ed stood alone in the sitting-room, gazing blankly at the ruins of a dream.

Unexpectedly, the telephone rang. Amidst all the chaos, that, at least, was working. Paul Ashburner was ringing to report that Pam had gone with Nicola in an ambulance to the hospital. He added that his wife had prepared a room for Ed and Pam. Other neighbours, Gerald and Vickie Keyes, would look after Sally and Johnnie. Overwhelmed by the way his neighbours were rallying around to help, Ed could only choke out his thanks.

After Ed had told Sally about the arrangements, he asked her if she knew where Johnnie was.

'I think he's in the downstairs toilet,' she replied. 'But he may be in your office looking for his homework books.'

Before he went to find his son, Ed quickly telephoned both his and Pam's parents to tell them what had happened. 'Try not to worry,' he told them. 'I'll keep you informed of any developments.'

As Ed walked towards the sitting-room door, Sally asked, 'Can I use the telephone, Dad?'

Preoccupied, he said, 'Yes, but be quick about it. Mr Keyes is on his way to collect you and Johnnie.'

Left alone, Sally picked up the telephone. She could barely wait to tell her new boyfriend the news but, when he answered, she did her best to play it cool and not sound too dramatic. 'You won't be able to pick me up at my house tonight,' she announced. 'My sister's burnt the whole place down and I'm staying with the Keyes.'

After a brief pause, the boy replied curtly, 'I don't want to get involved in this. Your sister must be cooky! Count me out! I just don't want the hassle of it!' Then he put down the phone.

*   *   *

In the distance, there was the sharp sound of quick foot-steps echoing down a long corridor, a metallic clang and then silence. Near by, a man was talking soothingly to a crying child. Close to me was the low humming noise of what I assumed was some form of room heater. Despite feeling drugged and woozy, I knew from the unmistakable smell of strong disinfectant that I was lying on a hospital bed.

I opened my eyes and gazed around the stark white room. To my astonishment, a young policeman was sitting unobtrusively in one corner. He was staring at me. I was suddenly conscious that the night-gown I was wearing was far too small so that the velcro didn't hold it together and much of my back was exposed.

'What are you doing here?' I asked him.

'You've been given a sedative and brought to the hospital because you were in shock,' he replied curtly. 'You'll be taken into custody soon and you'll have to make a statement.' Then he leaned forward and, unable to restrain himself, demanded, 'Why did you do it?'

I stared back at him blankly. There was nothing I could say so I merely shook my head slowly. I felt nothing – no shock, no remorse, no guilt.

The door opened and Mum walked in with a nurse. I saw at a glance how drained and miserable she was, but I didn't want to talk to her and so I turned away.

'Oh, Nicola,' she said plaintively, 'what have you done now? What can any of us do to help you?'

It was disappointing that she wasn't angry. Why didn't she lose her temper? Why didn't she snap, hit me, swear, break down? What made her so cloyingly, pathetically nice?

There was no need for me to answer nor the time for her to say anything else, because in the corridor I could hear Dad's raised voice, berating the whole medical profession. 'And another thing, doctor,' he was shouting, 'just over a week ago my wife phoned the psychiatric unit to fix another appointment. She was so worried by Nicola and was at her wits' end. They kept putting her off and then reluctantly – and I tell you the truth, it was reluctantly – they made an appointment for next week, even though my wife kept on telling them it was an emergency. Well, that's too late now, isn't it? Now Nicola's set fire to the house. That's what's happened. Well I've had it with the lot of you. So don't talk to me any more about trick cyclists and experts in . . . whatever you call it. Oh, yes, emotional illness! That's what you think it is, don't you?'

Dad stormed into the room red-faced with fury. He pointed straight at me and, spitting out the words, declared, 'You bloody horrible little bitch! Well, you've really done it this time. You've ruined our home – Sally's home, Johnnie's home, your mother's home and my home. That's what you've done. You wanted to destroy everything, didn't you? Well, I'll tell you this, all that you've destroyed is yourself.'

'Oh, please don't, Ed!' Mum pleaded, putting an hand on his arm.

Dad pushed her arm away and barked, 'Come on, Pam. Let's get out of here.' And, with that, he rushed out of the room. Mum briefly glanced at me, her eyes filled with tears, and then she hurried after Dad whose footsteps I could hear thudding down the corridor.

There had been total hatred in Dad's face and he looked as though he wanted to kill me. For the first time, I was really frightened. I didn't know what was going to happen to me. Despite the policeman sitting in the corner, it hadn't occurred to me till then that I might be arrested or anything like that. I'd just assumed that, when Dad turned up, he'd sort the whole thing out and take me home.

A few moments later, Nanny and Grandad came into the room. They both looked strained and tearful. Nanny rushed up to the bed and, as she hugged and kissed me, she sobbed, 'Why did you do it, Nicola?'

'I don't know, Nanny. I just wanted to die.'

'Well, you mustn't worry, Nicola,' she said softly. 'Whatever happens, your grandad and I will give everything we've got to make you well again.'

There was no time for her to say anything more, because a policewoman walked in and said to Nanny and Grandad, 'I'm sorry but you'll have to leave now. We've got to take this young woman down to the police station.'

As soon as my grandparents had left, the policewoman told me to take off my hospital night-dress and put back on my jumper and plimsolls.

I glanced at the young policeman who was still sitting in the corner and said, 'Do you mean right here and now?'

'Of course,' the policewoman replied tartly.

I looked again at the policeman and he turned his head away to face the wall. Well aware of how repulsive my fat body looked when naked, I quickly pulled off the night-dress and, while trying to shield my huge breasts and bulging stomach with my flabby arms, I attempted to yank the jumper over my head. I made such a mess of it that the policewoman had to give me a hand. I was so confused that she even had to tie the laces of my plimsolls.

As she did so, she said, 'What made you do it?' Giving me no time to reply, she went on, 'Your parents' house is devastated. The damage must run into thousands. What on earth got into you? Why did you do it?'

I stared fixedly at my shoelaces and said nothing.

Escorted by the two police officers, I was then taken out of the hospital to a waiting police car and driven to Bexleyheath Police Station.

There, the policewoman led me into a small office. Behind a heavy desk, cluttered with half-empty coffee-cups and overflowing ashtrays, sat a large, middle-aged detective. He'd taken off his jacket and had rolled up the sleeves of his blue shirt. The top two buttons were undone and his black tie hung loosely around his neck. Under his arms were dark perspiration stains.

Next to the detective sat a young uniformed policeman whose job apparently was to transcribe our conversation into his bulging notepad.

I was told to sit down and the policewoman who had brought me from the hospital asked if I'd like a cup of coffee. I nodded gratefully.

Then the questions began. The detective had a soft, kindly voice and a strong pleasant face with penetrating green eyes. When he wasn't smoking, his nicotined hands played constantly with a much-chewed lead pencil. He was not at all frightening and I tried hard to give him all the information he wanted.

But all the time, as I was wearing only my baggy black jumper, I felt terribly cold. So I was relieved when the policewoman brought in the coffee. I held the mug I was given firmly in both my hands to warm them. As I sipped the unexpectedly bitter drink, I stared at the room's bare yellowing walls and the single, curtainless window. In one corner of the ceiling, there was a large patch of festering damp. The whole room smelt rank and musty – an unappetizing mixture of stale perspiration and cigarette smoke. I could feel an asthma attack coming on. It always happened when I was under severe stress.

After what seemed like hours of questioning, the detective said patiently, 'Well, Nicola, we have some details of what happened today. You won't or perhaps can't tell us why you set fire to your parents' house and so what I want to do now is to find out some things about your past. Perhaps that way we'll be able to discover what happened to cause you to break the law. You see, Nicola, we want to find out what is the best solution for you. There's a reasonable chance the court will recommend psychiatric treatment that will help you, but first you've got to help us. Is that understood, Nicola?'

I nodded and the questions continued. Occasionally, as he busily took down my answers, the young policeman would interrupt to say, 'Could you repeat that?' At other times, he'd scribble furiously on a separate piece of paper in a desperate effort to force his battered ball-point pen to continue working.

At last the prolonged interview came to an end. 'As it's Saturday today,' the detective announced, 'you can't appear before the magistrates until Monday morning and so you'll be spending the next couple of nights in police custody.'

The policewoman took me down to the tiny, elongated cell. The floor was grey concrete and the white tiled walls were covered with graffiti. Very high up, there was a solitary, small barred window through which I could see that it was dark outside. Running along one side of the cell was a wooden bench in which was fitted a white porcelain toilet. Perched next to it was a roll of crinkly white toilet paper. There was also a neatly folded brown blanket. How can I sleep here? I thought. There isn't even a proper bed. Why don't Mum and Dad come and get me?

Beneath the bench, I noticed a wire grille covered with tiny particles of dust and fluff. This presumably marked the end of a heating duct. But it didn't seem to be working because I was shivering with cold.

'Take off your clothes,' the policewoman said.

Meekly, I did as I was told.

'Bend over,' she said, pulling a rubber glove over her right hand. 'I have to check you haven't concealed any drugs.'

After this further indignity, I listened numbly as the policewoman said, 'Because you're considered to be potentially suicidal, Nicola, there'll be a policeman on guard outside your cell all night. But, so you can get a good night's sleep, a doctor will be coming soon to give you a couple of sleeping pills.'

After I'd taken these, I sat disconsolately on the hard wooden bench, trying to keep warm by wrapping the blanket tightly around me. In the distance, I could hear the sound of people coming and going in the police station. I could hear it all and yet it seemed so unreal. I was so lonely and frightened. Why had I been locked up in this hideous police cell? I couldn't even phone anybody to find out what was going on.

Why aren't Mum and Dad here? I thought in my despair. Why aren't they sorting everything out? Why have they left me here all alone? Why haven't they organized a proper bed?

As I began to drift off into sleep, I started to think back to the girl I once had been. What happened to her? It was all so long ago. Where are you now, Nicola? Where have you gone?

# CHAPTER TWELVE

## *Prison*

That Saturday night, Ed and Pam stayed with their neighbours, the Ashburners. Badly shaken by the day's traumatic events, they could only nibble at the wholesome dinner that had been prepared for them. As they tried to avoid talking either about Nicola or the fire, their conversation was stilted and diffident. It was a relief for both of them when they were able to make their excuses and go upstairs to bed.

Pam hadn't as yet been to see the house, but she needed to escape from the horrific reality of what had happened and was soon asleep. Ed, on the other hand, was unable to rest. A flood of anxious thoughts and memories churned violently through his mind. Suddenly, as he tried to conceal his sobbing, his whole body began to shake.

Instantly, Pam was awake. 'What's the matter with you?' she asked impatiently.

'Oh, my poor Nicola, Pam,' Ed cried. 'It's so awful. What are we going to do? Poor, poor Nicola! She's going to prison. Our daughter's going to prison!'

This was the moment when Pam felt she needed her husband to be strong and yet he was lying next to her, blubbering like a child. 'Oh, you weak man!' she exclaimed. 'Go to sleep!'

Eventually, Ed managed to stifle his grief-stricken crying, but he lay awake, his whole body trembling, throughout that long night.

\*     \*     \*

I was awakened in the morning by a policewoman bringing me a mug of tea and a bacon sandwich. I devoured it ravenously.

Later, I was taken out of my cell, first to be fingerprinted and then to be photographed. A camera was set up on a crude tripod and I was told to look at the policeman and nobody else. Then I had to turn sideways for another photograph to be taken. As I was having these mug shots taken, it suddenly struck me as ironic that there had once been a time when I posed in front of a camera because people were paying me to model for them.

After I had been taken back to my cell, I was told that I was going to be transferred to another police station where there were facilities for women.

But I was given an almost identical cell, although much darker than the first. After I'd been locked in, I lay on the bench and pulled the blanket around me. I spent hours and hours there. There was just the time and the waiting. I was so used to doing things when I wanted to occupy myself, but in the cell there was nothing I could do. I couldn't even read. The light was terribly dim and I couldn't concentrate. So I just slept fitfully.

*　　　*　　　*

On Sunday morning, Ed and Pam went to their local police station to make statements. They were there several hours, unaware that Nicola was locked in a cell below. As far as they knew, she had been taken straight from the hospital to Holloway Prison. Before they left, the duty policeman asked them to provide some clothes for Nicola. It wasn't going to be easy. All her things had been destroyed in the fire. Fortunately, when they returned to their neighbours for lunch, Pam Ashburner said she'd find some suitable clothes for Nicola. After lunch, Ed and Pam dropped these off at the police station and then they went to the house.

Ed saw the colour drain from Pam's face. Black debris and charred remains were strewn all over the patio and the terraced rose beds that led to the lawn. Spread half-way across the waterfall and pond was the family's mud-trampled orange and blue tent. Protruding from the mounds of black, wet filth were several shiny pieces of metal. Tentatively, they picked them out. They were just a few of the hundred and thirty medals that Nicola had won at dancing festivals.

The light was beginning to fade when they went back into the house. Having looked around and seen the horrors there, Pam turned to Ed and said quite calmly, 'Well, what are we going to do?'

'The first thing,' Ed replied confidently, 'is to get these sodden carpets up. Tony Dean's in carpets. I'll give him a ring.'

'But there's no electricity, Eddie,' Pam protested. 'We've got to have some light in here. I think I'll phone Mrs Green to see if she's got a camping lamp.'

The telephone calls were made. Tony Dean not only promised to deal with the carpets, he also found an electrician and a builder who could both start work and would arrive with him at eight the following morning. Within the hour, the loyal Mrs Green arrived with her husband and a large lamp.

It was the start of an overwhelming flood of kindness and practical help that the Owens were to receive from both their own friends and those of their children. These volunteer helpers stripped wallpaper, cleaned smoke-blackened ceilings, delivered cooked meals and, as demanded by the insurers, carefully sifted through the evil-smelling, water-logged debris to find surviving oddments of an item of furniture or some precious possession to prove it had actually been in the house at the time of the fire.

\*    \*    \*

After my lonely night in the cell, I was brought a cup of tea and a fried-egg sandwich which, because I was used to gorging, I just stuffed greedily into my mouth.

A policewoman then brought me a parcel of clothes and told me to get dressed so I could be taken to the magistrates' court.

When I'd opened the parcel, I didn't recognize any of the dresses or underwear and so I said to the wardress, 'Where did these come from?'

'Your mother dropped them in yesterday.'

'Why didn't she come to see me?'

'She took the clothes to her local police station but you were here,' the policewoman replied. 'But, in any case, you're not allowed to have visitors.'

I didn't believe her. I knew that for some reason or other my mother had decided she didn't want to see me.

When I'd dressed, I was taken out of the cell and joined two other women. They looked very rough with unwashed hair and badly crinkled clothes. They didn't even glance at me, but they had the same worn-out look that I was sure I also had.

The three of us were led into a green transit van with barred windows. It was cold inside and smelt musty. There were trampled cigarette ends on the floor and the cracked vinyl seats were badly ripped.

We sat in silence as the van drove off. It seemed so strange, driving through the area where I had lived for so long and yet knowing that I was no longer free to walk those familiar streets. The once beautiful and talented dancer was now locked in an unmarked police van heading for the magistrates' court.

The van approached the court from the rear and pulled up in front of a pair of large metal doors which slowly swung open. After we'd been driven into what seemed to be an enclosed garage, the doors were firmly closed. Then the three of us were escorted from the van into the

140 .

building where we were each given a separate cell beneath the court-room.

The wardress who locked me in was very kind to me and brought me a cup of coffee. Although she had a glass eye, she was very attractive with vivid ginger hair and a slender figure. I felt much better knowing that she was there.

I sat alone on the long wooden bench in the large cell, facing the heavy bolted door. It was cold, stark and depressing there. Previous occupants had scribbled crude messages on the rough plastered walls. One of the light bulbs made a constant buzzing noise because the filament was just about to snap. Apart from this, I couldn't hear much, other than the odd sound of laughter coming from an office along the corridor.

Eventually, I heard the clanking of keys. The door was unlocked and I was taken out of the cell, led up some stairs and met Mary, a sympathetic CID officer who was in charge of my case. We waited together outside the court-room.

When it was time for my case to be heard, I was escorted into the court and told to remain standing inside a small boxed area. Sitting at the high bench in front of me were three middle-aged magistrates. I glanced around the court-room and to one side saw Mum and Dad sitting bolt upright, frozen like statues.

I was charged with arson and pleaded guilty. When I was asked my address, I replied, 'No fixed abode,' because I assumed that Mum and Dad had disowned me.

Dad then stood up and was shown to the witness-box where he said something about there always being a home for me with 'my wife and I'. But I didn't take in what he was saying. I couldn't even look at him.

I was told that I was to be remanded in custody for a week so that further evidence could be collected and a report prepared. It meant nothing to me. I didn't care that I was going to be taken to prison. I seemed to have lost all feeling. Inside, I was totally numb.

I was then taken back to the cell and the moment I'd been dreading arrived when I was told that my parents had come to see me. I can't remember much about that meeting, except that my father cuddled me and my mother cried all the time. Then all of a sudden they were gone and I was alone in the cell.

\*　　\*　　\*

Distraught and drawn, Ed and Pam made their way slowly out of the magistrates' court. They were almost at the front door when a young policewoman came up to them, introduced herself and said she was involved in Nicola's case. 'Do you have a solicitor, Mr Owen?' she asked.

'Not for anything like this,' Ed replied.

'I hope you understand that it isn't for me to make a recommendation,' she said, obviously concerned. 'But I would suggest you have a word with somebody at Smythe and Notcutt. Their offices are just along the road on the left. They'll certainly be able to help in a case like this.'

Ed thanked her warmly and, acting on her advice, they immediately went to the office where they explained to Mr Smythe, a senior partner, what had happened. He was a middle-aged, agreeable man who impressed Ed with the quickness of his mind and his decisiveness.

Having assimilated the key facts, Mr Smythe said, 'I would like to keep this first meeting short as there is still time for me to go down to the court to have a word with Nicola.' Then, having made an appointment for the next meeting, he showed them out and went straight off to interview his new client.

Ed and Pam returned to the chaos of the house. Within minutes, two CID officers arrived.

'We've had a report from the fire brigade,' one of them told Ed, 'that suggests the possibility that petrol or some flammable chemical could have been used either to start the fire or to have intensified it. The report says that the fire took hold very quickly and that it generated an extraordinary heat.'

'There were no chemicals or petrol in the house, officer,' Ed responded. 'But there were six or seven cardboard filing containers filled with papers that were stacked in the loft, just beyond the hatch and immediately over Nicola's bedroom, which is where the fire was started.'

Ed took them to have a look and it was easy to see how the stack of stored paper sent a pyramid of fire straight up towards the bituminous roofing felt. Using a stepladder, the two CID men clambered into the loft and peered around. Once they had left, nothing more was heard of the petrol or chemicals theory.

\*　　\*　　\*

Back in the cell, I was visited by Mr Smythe, a solicitor that my parents had contacted. After asking me many questions, he told me that I would be going to Holloway Prison for a week but after that it might be possible for me to be released on bail.

'Although you're not yet eighteen, Nicola,' he said, 'I shall be applying for legal aid on your behalf. It's almost certain that you will have had your eighteenth birthday before your case comes to trial.'

When the solicitor had left, the wardress with the glass eye came into the cell and asked if I was all right. I assured her I was.

'That's good,' she said cheerily. 'It's going to be quite a time before the prison van arrives to collect you.'

Despite all the drama of the situation, most of the time had been spent just waiting for things to happen. Everything took such a long time. It was something that I soon accepted. After all, I had nothing else to do but wait.

After I'd spent four hours sitting in the cell, I was taken outside and led with another girl into the same green prison van. There was a male driver and a grim-faced wardress who, I assumed, was from Holloway. On the way to the prison, we stopped at various courts to collect other prisoners. The funny thing was that we all looked dirty, presumably because the rest of them, like me, had been unable to wash. Although nobody spoke during the journey, there was some sort of unspoken friendliness between us. We all had at least some idea of what the rest of us were going through.

Without warning, the van pulled off the busy main road and drove a short distance to some forbidding gates set in massive red-brick walls surmounted with coils of barbed wire. Almost immediately, the gates parted in the middle, slowly being pulled back by two expressionless men in navy uniforms. The van moved forward and stopped in front of a second pair of gates until the first ones had been closed and locked.

After we had passed through the second gates, the van crept towards, and then around, a vast piece of modern sculpture. At first glance, it looked like a man but there was a large hole in the middle and a complete lack of detail. There was no face, no fingers, no limbs, no identity – simply a grey lump of lifeless granite standing in stark contrast to what appeared to be a never-ending maze of red brick.

The van halted and the prison wardress jumped out of the front seat and waited impatiently for the driver to unlock the side door. I was the first one out. The long, uncomfortable ride in the stale-smelling van had made me nauseous and so I gratefully gulped in the cool air.

The prison building seemed made up of square, disjointed blocks studded with an abundance of narrow oblong windows. My vision seemed sharpened, as if I were looking through a magnifying glass, and I felt overwhelmed by the stark angular shapes that jutted harshly across the skyline. It was late afternoon and the darkening sky was filled with angry, unfriendly grey clouds that were trying to block out the weak February sun. In the descending

The model child at six weeks old with Mum and Dad.

A local fancy-dress competition. Even when small, I loved to perform.

Aged seven, with my brother, Johnnie, and sister, Sally.

The Witch from *Hansel and Gretel*, aged thirteen. I was so involved in this performance that I frightened some children in the audience.

Looking like a
prima ballerina at
fourteen.

These cups were
won six months after
breaking my leg.

Taken by a local
hairdresser who
visited my school
to give us a careers
talk and asked me
to model for his
salon.
*(© Graham Webb
International)*

With Johnnie, on a family holiday in Dorset. The increase in my weight was already beginning to show.

With Sally, on a day out together in Hastings. I was seeing a psychiatrist by this stage.

Taken by a teacher from a nearby boys' school who, despite my rather haunted expression, asked me to pose for his pupils so they could paint a girl's face.

A summer holiday in Majorca; I am wearing a wig, having shaved my head just before we left.

Still in Majorca, this loose top covers my deliberately inflicted sunburn.

A letter sent to my parents from my cell in Holloway. Because it was shortly after I had slashed my wrist, it was written by somebody else.

In replying to this letter, please write on the envelope:—

Number........... Name..................

H.M. Prison,
Parkhurst Road,
Holloway,
LONDON, N.7.

Dear Mum + Dad,
I'm sorry that I am not writing this letter, and I've kindly asked a friend to write it for me as I have had an accident. I will endeavour to explain how it came about.
On Saturday after Dad's visit I was very upset, I got the impression that you would like to have me out of the way. Looking back I realise it is not so but the depression was building up inside me. On Saturday night about quarter to six I picked up my aid of glass bottle and smashed it against the window and with the broken glass cut my wrist. I was taken to Doctors surgery where the Doctor told me I would have to go to hospital. When

Mum brought this picture of my restored bedroom to show me during my time in the strip cell at Holloway. I wasn't allowed to keep it because of the chemicals it contained. It was thought that I might try to commit suicide by eating it.

36 Camden Road – the rear of the house after the fire,
showing the patched tiles where the roof had been smashed
to prevent the house exploding.

With Mum
and Dad about
six months
after my
release from
Holloway.

A dream come true: the day of my marriage to Guy,
7 December 1991. (© *Mr Ricky Turrell*)

dusk, the prison took on an unreal quality that didn't soften but accentuated its ugliness.

I was joined by the other women prisoners whose faces looked tense and strained. Not even their eyes betrayed the feeling of despair we'd all felt at the outset of our journey. We had left our emotions at the gate and, to survive, all we had to do now was to obey orders. Everybody concentrated on watching the wardress unlock the thick outer door with a large key selected from the enormous bunch attached by a long metal chain to her belt.

Once we were inside, the door was relocked. Through a square, concrete-floored hallway and up a steep flight of steps, we followed the wardress as her stout frame swayed from side to side, making the bunch of keys clang heavily against her hips. It was a sound that was fast becoming familiar to me.

At the top of the stairs, we turned left and came to another locked door with a small reinforced window. As the door opened, a babble of voices cut the silence and we entered a room already half-full of women dressed in the regulation blue towelling, wrap-over dresses. The door was locked behind us and, still panting from the exhausting climb up the stairs, I made my way to an empty chair.

Some of the women chattered whilst others stared unseeingly ahead of them. A thin, washed-out blonde was sitting on a table with her feet resting on a chair as she cradled her large swollen belly in her gnarled hands. She was talking to a girl, sitting three tables away, about a previous abortion. As she listened wide-eyed to every word, the girl determinedly chewed an imaginary piece of gum.

A dark-haired woman sat on a radiator staring through the barred window at the empty exercise-yard below. There were black hollows around her eyes and she nervously bit into the dead skin of her chapped lips. She held her gown tightly round her with two hands. Her whole body was shaking. As if to hide this, she was rocking herself

145

backwards and forwards, apparently unaware that as she completed each movement her shoulder smashed hard against the window.

At last, my name was called and I was led out of the waiting-room into a similar one opposite. Two elderly wardresses put me through the admission procedure with the automatic efficiency that comes only with many years of experience. I was undressed completely and given a blue robe that I gratefully pulled around me. I was told to bend my head and a pair of cold hands parted my hair in several places to search for signs of lice or fleas. A blue shoe-bag was filled with a bar of soap, a transparent sachet of yellow shampoo, a piece of white cloth that was presumably meant to be a flannel, and a toothbrush. This collection was given to me with my number. From that moment on, I was to be known officially only by that number. Nicola Owen became D02572 c/o Her Majesty's Prison.

Thirty-nine women were admitted that day and so it was a very slow process. At one stage, we were served high tea – two pieces of sliced white bread, a pat of margarine, one cold hard-boiled egg that had nasty brown bits in it, and a pink, melting ice-cream that seeped into the edges of the bread. A white plastic mug was filled with tea from an enormous metal teapot that looked more like a watering-can. Those who wanted sugar had a small spoonful ladled in from a white plastic container. I was to discover later that sugar was a luxury and was rationed to one spoonful per prisoner per day.

The room was very warm and the atmosphere was oppressive. I had a terrible headache and my only desire was to sleep. The events of the previous few days had left me feeling absolutely shattered.

At last, everybody had been checked in and the next step was to have a brief medical inspection. The doctor cursorily asked if I was pregnant, on the pill or had recently been given an abortion. I was stood on the scales, my heart was listened to and then I had to lie on a table and open my legs so that I could be examined for venereal disease. As the doctor completed my records, I saw that on the top there was a small note – 'Suicidal tendencies. Recommend psychiatrist.'

I was then allowed a five-minute bath in the presence of yet another wardress. The water wasn't very warm, the soap didn't lather and the towel I was given barely went round me. I was rapidly getting used to the humiliating experiences. I wasn't embarrassed. I didn't care what was happening to me.

At half-past eight that night, I was issued with a bundle of bed linen and taken along a corridor to a room that I was to share with seven other girls. Automatically, we started to make up our beds. There were four double bunks, one in each corner of the room. In the centre, there were two tables, each surrounded by four upright chairs. Against one wall, there was a small washbasin and a plastic mirror. Opposite was a partitioned-off toilet.

Two of the girls started writing letters, while the other five carefully rolled their own cigarettes from small quantities of tobacco and pieces of toilet paper. When they'd finished, they shouted through the hatch in the door for a wardress to give them a light.

I climbed slowly into my bunk and pulled the stiff sheets around me, thinking, Nicola, don't look back now. Forget the past. It's gone. I willed myself to keep calm, but the fluttering panic in my chest kept rising and I started to shake. My tightly closed eyes burned and the lump in my throat was close to choking me as I tried not to cry. Exhausted, I could hold back no longer. The tears welled up and rolled down my face. What a mess! What an evil person I had become! How I longed for the return of the old Nicola. I felt so lonely and ached for the touch of my parents. I wanted to go home and cocoon myself in their love.

\*    \*    \*

That Monday evening, Ed stayed at the Ashburners' but Pam decided that she was going to sleep in their fire-damaged house. Despite the appalling state it was in, she didn't want to be anywhere else. She didn't get undressed but just lay alone on the settee in the fire-blackened lounge of what had been, but a few days before, her perfect family home.

# CHAPTER THIRTEEN

## *On Bail*

The loud, continuous ringing of a bell rudely jolted me back into the unhappy reality of my new situation. The harsh sound seemed to reverberate through me as I lay on my back staring at the grey ceiling. It was half-past seven in the morning and light outside. Although it was cloudy, the sun was managing to seep through in places and a beam of light shone through the window projecting a striped rectangle on the wall opposite.

The bell stopped as abruptly as it had started. Coming from the other bunks, I could hear mumbled protests and a few deep groans. Most of the girls promptly rolled over and went back to sleep again. Nobody made any effort to get up. There was nothing to get up for.

A few minutes past eight, there was a banging at the door. The hatch was unlocked and pulled down. A woman with a pale-skinned face devoid of all make-up peered in and shouted, 'OK, you lot! Up you get! Breakfast in five minutes!'

I pulled back my bedding and climbed down awkwardly from the bunk. Just as I'd finished dressing, there was a jangling of keys and the door swung open.

'Breakfast in the dining-room.'

I went to the door and followed the long stream of girls coming from the other cells into a large room filled with rows of tables and chairs. I collected a white plastic plate which was filled with two slices of bread, some margarine, a peculiar-shaped sausage, and a knife and fork. In the other hand, I was given a blue plastic bowl full of lukewarm, watery porridge.

I found a place to sit down. All the time I was eating, women and girls kept pouring into the room until all the tables were full. After a mug of tea, we were ushered back into our cells. Breakfast had taken less than fifteen minutes.

For the next half an hour, supervised by a wardress, we swept and then washed our cell floor. Then we were again locked in. Feeling very low, I climbed back into bed and shut my eyes. But I couldn't keep out either the constant shouting of girls at windows all over the prison or the echoing footsteps and crashing keys of the heavy-footed wardresses.

Several hours later, I was taken to see one of the prison governors, who asked me if there was anything I needed and told me that my parents had been informed of my whereabouts. He also asked if I had a solicitor and if I'd be applying for legal aid. To both these questions, I nodded my head. I was then escorted back to my cell in time for lunch.

We ate a yellow curry with mushy rice, followed by a piece of dry sponge covered in lumpy custard. Despite its unappetizing appearance, the meal was quite pleasant with generous helpings. But it lay heavily on my stomach and left me feeling extremely tired.

Later that afternoon, we were told to fold our bedding. Then we were escorted in turn to the permanent wing considered most suitable for each of us. I was taken to C1, a unit for inmates with psychiatric problems. It was known to the rest of Holloway as 'The Funny Farm'. The dormitory had pink and white walls with matching pink covers on the five beds. Each of us had our own small locker and wardrobe.

After I'd made my bed, I sat on it and looked at my four fellow inmates who were all sitting around the table.

One was a very tall, blonde lady in her mid-thirties who, though still attractive, had a tired, dissipated look

150

about her. I was astonished to discover that she had been put in prison on a drinks charge. She was very nervous all the time and was constantly smoking roll-up cigarettes so that her fingers were stained burnt yellow with the nicotine.

Another was a dark-haired girl who, every time she spoke, clicked her tongue. She had a phobia about cleanliness. Much of the time she was in the cell, she spent washing and rewashing her hands and clothes.

There was also a woman who appeared to be very old and was in prison on a vagrancy charge. I was to discover that every single night without fail she would wet the bed. In the morning, the stench of urine was overpowering. She was absolutely filthy and never bathed.

The fourth was a woman called Lofty. From the back, she looked like a little girl. She was very short, had her hair in a pig-tail and wore full length white socks. But when she turned round, she had the face of a really old woman. Her skin was heavily wrinkled and she had no teeth. It was quite a shock, but she was not unpleasant. She just had a yearning to be loved and so demanded your attention constantly.

Then there was me.

\*       \*       \*

That evening, friends were helping Pam and Ed clear the dining-room. From the bookcase, Pam picked up a coloured photograph of Nicola wearing one of her dance costumes. For a moment, Pam stared at it and then she suddenly burst into a flood of tears. Nobody could comfort or console her. She just cried and cried. Even when the doctor arrived half an hour later, Pam was still crying.

'I can't believe my daughter is in Holloway with all those awful people,' she sobbed to the doctor.

'All those women, Mrs Owen,' he said gently, 'are somebody's mum or daughter.'

'I know and I'm ever so sorry,' she cried, adding unexpectedly, 'But I just want my dog.'

Emma was brought back to the house from the neighbours who had been looking after her and Pam was prescribed Valium.

The tranquillizer really helped her and took away the fear of what might lie ahead. At least on the surface, Pam appeared very calm, whereas Ed was becoming increasingly anxious and uptight. It was fortunate for their relationship that they complemented each other. When one was down, the other always seemed able to help.

The following day, they went together to visit Mr Smythe, the solicitor.

'We shall need medical reports,' he told them, 'if an application for bail is to succeed.'

'Well, there's Dr Goble. He's a psychiatrist and there's also Dr Sangster,' Pam suggested. 'They've both seen a lot of Nicola.'

'I'm sure they are both excellent doctors,' Mr Smythe said, 'but we shall need the opinion of a doctor who is well known to the court. I know a Dr Morley who is a very good man and much experienced in dealing with matters of this sort. I think it would be most helpful in this situation if we were able to obtain his opinion.'

Ed and Pam readily agreed to this.

'Please would you be kind enough,' Mr Smythe then said, 'when next you visit Nicola, to tell her to expect a visit from Dr Morley.'

'I'll be seeing her tomorrow,' Pam said.

In fact, Pam visited Nicola every afternoon she was in Holloway. It was a terrifying ordeal for her. Each day, before she left home, she took a Valium to ensure that she didn't break down in front of her daughter. But the experience was so heartbreaking that, as soon as she left Nicola, she would burst into tears.

One day, when she was driving to Holloway, Pam was stopped on the approach road to the Blackwall Tunnel by a police motorcyclist.

'And what do you think you're doing, madam?' he asked. 'Where are you off to that makes you want to break the speed limit and overtake a policeman?'

'I'm sorry,' Pam replied. 'But I didn't know you were a policeman!'

'And where might you be going in such a hurry?'

'I'm on the way to visit my daughter in Holloway Prison.'

'Oh yes, madam,' the policeman said mockingly. 'Holloway, you say? Your daughter is it?'

'Yes,' Pam replied patiently, glancing at her watch.

'And what, might I enquire, is your daughter doing in Holloway?'

'She set fire to our house.'

The policeman was clearly taken aback. 'You know I can check on that?' he asked, with no trace of his previous mocking tone.

'Yes, please do. The address is thirty-six Camden Road, Bexley, and the name is Owen. My daughter is Nicola Owen.'

Painstakingly, he wrote the details in his notebook and then, peering down at her, said, 'All right. I shall check this out, but it's still no excuse for breaking the speed limit. You were doing fifty-five when you passed me. Do you know what the speed limit is on this stretch of road?'

'No, I'm sorry, but I don't.'

The policeman declined to provide the information, saying instead, 'Get along now and keep to the speed limit or you won't arrive at wherever it is you're going.'

With relief, Pam thanked the policeman, presuming that was the end of the matter. (A few weeks later, she received a summons for having broken the speed limit.)

Later that same day, as Ed and a couple of friends were sifting through the rubbish outside, two workmen came out of the house carrying a heavy trunk.

'This was up in the attic, Ed,' one of them said. 'It's a bit fire-blackened, but it's the only thing up there that's survived. What's in it?'

Ed gingerly opened the trunk. On top lay the witch's costume. He carefully lifted it up and then, one by one, took out the rest of Nicola's dance costumes. All were perfect.

'How can it be?' Ed mused. 'How can it be that these are the only things in the whole house that haven't been touched by the fire?'

\*　　\*　　\*

After I'd been in Holloway for a week, I was taken back to the magistrates' court to be told I was to be remanded in custody for a further seven days so another psychiatrist's opinion could be obtained. I then had the same long wait for the prison van to take me back to Holloway where the whole long-winded admittance procedure was repeated.

During the second week, I tried to sleep as much as I could so that the time would go quicker. Because I was on remand, I was still allowed visitors. Mum often brought somebody I knew with her and she did her best to cheer me up but, though I knew she was cheerful for my sake, I could see she was showing signs of unbearable tension.

Every day, she told me how the builders were getting on with the house and how it would soon be habitable again. During one visit, she said I was going to be interviewed by Dr Morley, a top psychiatrist. If his report was favourable, I would be allowed out on bail.

Shortly afterwards, I was seen by the doctor, who was a charming and patient man. He asked me a lot about my early years. I did my best to answer his questions.

I told him that I'd always been tense as a child and had wet the bed until I was eight. When he enquired if anything changed with the onset of puberty, I said that, when I was about fourteen, I began to have periods of depression which came out of the blue, sometimes lasting for a few minutes but other times going on for weeks. It was also about the same time that I started overeating and my weight increased dramatically. Dr Morley said he thought I would respond to psychiatric treatment and could be released on bail.

The following week, when I appeared in court, I was granted bail on my mother's surety of £500, subject to the conditions that Dr Morley had suggested – I had to live with my parents, to report twice a day to the police and, unless I was out in the company of my parents, I had to be indoors by seven o'clock each evening.

None of this worried me at the time. I was just happy not to be going back to prison. I was on a strange high, feeling better than I'd done for a long time as Mum drove me home.

When we arrived, I saw that it wasn't the house as I remembered it. A lot of repairs had already been done, but my bedroom wasn't there any more. It was just brick walls, charred black by oily smoke. The bathroom I'd used had been completely gutted. All the carpets had been removed and every room was damaged. There were builders everywhere – rewiring, decorating, wallpapering and painting.

Looking around, I wasn't really shocked. I had no feelings of remorse. I felt quite emotionless. But, deep inside, I was much more concerned about myself than the house because I knew that I wasn't right. The uncontrollable evil inside me had not gone away.

There seemed to be a good atmosphere in the house. Mum had got into a routine, working around the builders. Everybody was pulling together with the same feeling of comradeship that happens between the survivors of a catastrophe. I didn't feel as though I'd done anything wrong. It just seemed as though I'd made a dramatic gesture, but so what?

A young plumber was working at the house and, because I was quite vibrant and cheeky, I think he was fascinated by me. I hadn't had a boyfriend for three years and I suppose I developed a fixation about him. We enjoyed being with each other. So we wanted to go out and have fun.

But it was impossible for me. Not only had I been ordered by the court to be in by seven each evening but Mum was still watching me like a hawk, waiting for me to do anything that was even vaguely suspicious. That made me very irritable.

One evening, a fortnight after I'd been released on bail, Dad was away on one of his business trips. Things had really started to get on top of me and I felt I couldn't stand being in the house a minute longer.

'I'm just going out for a short walk,' I said to Mum.

'You'll have to make it quick, Nicola,' she replied. 'You've got to be back by seven and it's quarter-past six now.'

\* \* \*

Nicola didn't return at seven o'clock, nor at eight. Not knowing what had happened, Pam was frantic with worry. She knew that Nicola still wasn't right. The fortnight that she'd been back home from prison had been wearing and frightening. Half the house was still damaged and unsecured. During the day, it was swarming with builders and friends but, when they'd gone, Pam was often left alone with her two daughters. Johnnie was away at boarding-school and Ed was frequently away on business. That meant most of the responsibility for looking after Nicola fell on her. So concerned was she that, in the middle of the night, she'd creep along to Nicola's bedroom to check that she was still there.

Pam was given much moral support by Sally, who was sixteen and supposed to be studying for her O levels. But Sally was beginning to feel resentful of her elder sister. She liked routine and yet her routine was constantly being upset by Nicola. Her parents looked on her as being strong and reliable – 'Good old Sal' – but she didn't always feel so strong. There were moments when she needed someone to give her a cuddle and ask her how she was. But nobody seemed to have the time. Once Nicola's dancing successes had been the family obsession. Now it was Nicola's problems.

Pam and Sally had again agreed that they wouldn't tell Ed anything about Nicola's misdemeanours while he was away. There was nothing he could do and it would only make him angry. So, when Ed phoned at nine o'clock that evening, they didn't tell him that Nicola wasn't at home.

'I'll just have a quick word with Nicola,' Ed said to Pam.

'She's sound asleep, Ed, and I don't think it's fair to wake her up. Do you?'

'No, Pam, don't do that. I'll talk to her tomorrow night.'

At ten, Pam telephoned the police station to enquire if they knew anything of Nicola who, by not being at home, had broken a condition of her bail. The police had no news. Nor was there any when Pam phoned again at eleven and at midnight.

All night, Pam sat on the settee by the telephone waiting for it to ring.

Just after ten o'clock the next morning, a police constable called at the house. 'Mrs Owen?' he enquired.

'Yes,' Pam said anxiously.

'Your daughter, Nicola, has been arrested for shop-lifting.'

Pam was both bemused and relieved. 'Well, that doesn't sound like Nicola,' she said.

'Will you come along with me to the police station?'

'Of course I will.'

As Pam entered the police station, she was greeted by an inspector who was familiar with Nicola's case.

'Is it true that Nicola's been arrested for stealing?' Pam asked him.

'Is that what he told you?' the inspector asked, nodding to the police constable.

'Yes, but it's not true, is it?'

'Not at all. That young constable had to call at two houses about different cases and he seems to have managed to get them both mixed up.'

'But Nicola's here? Is she all right?'

'She's fine. She turned up early this morning at the police station to sign on. It was only after she'd left that the duty sergeant realized she was the girl who'd been reported missing and so he sent two policemen scampering down the road after her. She was brought back here, arrested and charged with breaking one of her bail conditions.'

The inspector accompanied Pam into the magistrates' court. After the charge had been read, Pam was asked to go into the witness-box.

'Mrs Owen, what do you think the reason was for Nicola staying out last night?' the chairman of the magistrates asked pleasantly.

'I think the restrictions may be a bit strict. She's allowed to go out with my husband and I, but what girl of seventeen only wants to be with her parents? She can't even go out with Sally, her sister.'

'Would you be prepared for your daughter, Sally, to be responsible for Nicola if they go out together and are allowed to return home at a later time?'

Pam thought for a moment and then replied, 'No, I'm sorry. Sally's only sixteen and I don't think it's fair to make her responsible for her sister.'

The three magistrates adjourned for a short while and, when they returned, the chairman announced, 'As a concession to Nicola, we will amend the conditions of bail to allow her to stay out until 9 p.m. every Friday.'

Pam was grateful. Given the circumstances, she felt that Nicola had been treated generously.

Her latest escapade left Nicola unmoved and unrepentant. However, it added greatly to the severe strain already afflicting her parents. Despite the daily tranquillizers she was taking, Pam felt very depressed and exhausted. Ed, who was having to spend long periods travelling around the country, was becoming increasingly tense and bad tempered. He looked so ill that Pam spoke about him to their doctor who prescribed some mild tranquillizers. But Ed refused to take them. He hated any kind of pill, only taking an aspirin if he was in severe pain.

A week after she'd stayed out all night, while Ed was again away from home on business, Nicola found her father's tranquillizers. She opened the bottle and swallowed every one of the pills.

\*     \*     \*

I remember Mum constantly slapping my face, telling me to wake up. But I just wanted to sleep and the next thing I knew I was having my stomach pumped again with that ghastly tube being pushed down my throat, making me gag. Then I passed out.

I woke up in a hospital bed. I didn't have any emotions. I was totally devoid of feelings. I didn't feel concerned or worried. And I quite liked that.

Dr Sangster visited me several times. Once, he came with a gynaecologist who prescribed a course of hormone pills. I began to feel better and, after a week in hospital, I thought it was time for me to go back home.

But Mum and Dad were in an awful state and said, 'We can't bear the stress of having you at home. We just don't know what you're going to do next. So you can't come back home yet.'

I was then told that I was going to be transferred to a mental hospital where I would be seen by Dr Goble, the same psychiatrist I'd seen several times before over the previous couple of years.

Oh, that's exciting, I thought. I haven't been in a mental hospital before.

It was a beautiful hospital in lovely grounds, but there was something terribly depressing about it and I immediately hated the place. The first thing I was told was that I wasn't allowed any visitors. I wasn't allowed to write any letters. I wasn't allowed to go out. All I could do was stare out of the window all day long as I sat in a ward full of people who were either senile or insane.

Despite all the weird things I'd been doing, I kept on saying to myself, I'm not mad. There's nothing wrong with me. I might be a bad lot, but I'm not mad.

When Dr Goble saw me he said that I had to stop taking the course of pills that had been prescribed because they would interfere with the strong doses of tranquillizers he was going to give me. These had a terrible effect on me. As soon as I'd had the first injection, I started to lose all my co-ordination and everything became a real effort. I kept crying and crying.

After a couple of days, I said to Dr Goble, 'I just don't want to be here. I'd rather go back to prison than stay in this place.'

'I agree with you,' he said. 'The only place you're going to get better is at home.'

My parents agreed that I could return home and that they'd take me each week to the hospital for my massive injection of the tranquillizer, Modicate.

This continued to make me feel awful. I seemed to have no control over my body. I couldn't even clean my teeth. I felt jittery. I shuffled up and down as though I was a sleepwalker. I couldn't sit still. When I tried to sleep, I would have to stand up. When I stood up, I wanted to lie down. My mouth hung open and I used to dribble. I kept twitching and, every now and then, my jaw would lock and I'd have to be taken to hospital to be given an injection to relax it.

When I complained, Dr Goble said, 'Well, you're going to have to put up with this for four weeks.'

Somehow, perhaps because I couldn't co-ordinate my hand movements and so couldn't eat, I lost quite a bit of weight. After about six weeks, when the weekly injection had been replaced by daily tablets of Modicate, I started to feel less jittery. But then the despair began and I didn't know what I was going to do or what was going to happen to me. All I wanted to do was to sleep.

# CHAPTER FOURTEEN

## *Strip Cell*

For my eighteenth birthday on 22 June, Mum bought me a new blue dress and I was taken with friends to an expensive night-club for a celebration dinner. It was a pleasant enough occasion. But I couldn't enjoy it. The drugs I was taking had turned me into a zombie.

My parents became so worried about me that they visited Dr Goble to ask him to reduce the doses he had prescribed. He agreed and there was an improvement. I was able to co-ordinate my body movements more, but I also began to experience strong waves of panic and desperation.

A week after my birthday, I appeared in Court Thirteen of the Old Bailey to plead guilty to the charge of arson. Wearing my pretty blue dress, I looked fairly slim and presentable. The judge listened to the police evidence and the written reports of psychiatrists, which seemed very long-winded and not very complimentary.

Dr Morley said that I was suffering from 'a personality disorder of considerable severity with hysterical features', but concluded that I might 'respond to prolonged psychiatric treatment' and that 'the environment of her home would be beneficial to her mental health.'

My funny old psychiatrist, Dr Goble, said more or less the same thing, calling me – rather patronizingly, I thought – 'a severely disturbed girl who will need continuous medical and psychiatric care and hospitalization where appropriate'.

As neither of them seemed to think very much of me, I couldn't fathom out why it was that Dr Goble seemed so desperate to keep me as one of his patients.

After all the clap-trap had finished, the judge reprimanded me, saying I'd committed a very serious offence and that I could have killed somebody. He concluded, 'Nicola Jane Owen, I am satisfied you were very emotionally upset at the time you committed arson and in genuine need of psychiatric treatment, and so I take an exceptional course in this case. I sentence you to two years' probation on the condition that you attend as an out-patient at the specified psychiatric clinic.'

Mr Giacomo, my barrister, and Mr Smythe, my solicitor, seemed very pleased with the verdict and everybody congratulated everybody else. As I left the court, all the drama was over but I knew that nobody had discovered what was wrong with me. I didn't believe that a psychiatrist or a probation officer could sort out the terrible feelings I had. It was most unsettling. All they'd done was to paper over the cracks. They thought they'd found a good solution, but it was no solution at all.

Outside the Old Bailey, there was a small army of press photographers. When we arrived home, journalists kept phoning and knocking on the door asking me to give an interview or pose for photographs. Next day, the case was big national news with headlines like 'Tragedy of girl who ate and ate', 'Dancer causes £25,000 blaze and goes free', 'Bulimia girl can't stop eating' and 'Young arsonist walks free from Court'.

None of it helped me. After the anticlimax of the trial, I didn't know what the hell I was going to do with my life.

Friends said, 'Why don't you try to get back to dancing?'

It was ridiculous. I was already overweight and I was again gorging enormous quantities of food. During the next fortnight, I put on over a stone in weight.

Mum said, 'You'll have to get yourself a job.'

I thought, How can I get a job when I'm not functioning properly, when I'm still on drugs?

Dad told me, 'You'll have to pull yourself together, Nicola, and start earning your living.'

I couldn't cope with this kind of harassment. When I visited the probation officer, I said, 'I must leave home. I must get away from all this pressure.'

She didn't understand me at all and replied, 'Put your name down on a council housing list.' What kind of help was that?

Every time I visited Dr Goble he merely gave me yet more Modicate or Valium to quieten me down for another week.

I felt that everything inside me was being suppressed and I knew that as soon as the drugs were taken away something was going to happen.

I decided to go and stay with my grandparents in Hastings, but I didn't seem to be able to settle for long in one place. After a week, I returned home. Then Mum told me that I had an interview on Monday for a job in a jeweller's shop in Orpington. I went back to stay with Nan in Hastings for the weekend and then on Monday I returned, as arranged, to meet Mum and Sally at Orpington Station.

It was a dull, grey day. In the back of the car, I changed into the loose-fitting smock-dress Mum had brought for me and then she drove me to the interview.

I don't know how I'm going to travel all this way to work, I thought. It's ridiculous. I don't want the job. But I determined to go ahead with it to please my parents and psychiatrist, just to prove to them that I really was making an effort to get well again.

While I went through the ordeal of the interview, Mum waited outside. Afterwards, as I climbed back into the car, she asked, 'Well, how did you get on?'

'I don't know,' I said. 'They're going to let me know.'

Going through the interview had taken an enormous effort and I thought, I'm not happy about this. I'm not well. How can I be expected to work when I'm not well?

As we were driving back home, Mum said, 'Why don't you pop into the local boutique and buy yourself a new dress?'

I did, but it didn't make me feel any happier. As I tried on the enormous tent dresses that covered up my grossness, all that I really wanted to buy were the clothes that I'd worn when I was slim.

I walked back home in the pouring rain. That afternoon, I was supposed to see my probation officer, but I phoned her and said, 'I can't make it. Can I see you tomorrow?'

'Fine,' she said and we arranged a new time.

I felt really low. I didn't feel suicidal, but I wanted to make a gesture to say, 'Look, you're carrying on as though nothing's happened. But I'm not right. And nobody will listen to me. Nobody will see that I'm still very fat, I'm still eating enormous quantities, I'm still very depressed and I'm still on all these tranquillizers. It's four weeks since my court case and nothing has happened. Nothing's going to happen. How can you talk about my going to work and getting back to normal? Nobody's listening to me and nobody's noticed.' Then a thought came to me: when I set fire to the house, at least people tried for a time to find out what was wrong with me.

A carpenter was working upstairs, Sally was in her bedroom, Dad was away on business, Mum was doing some typing in the office and Johnnie, who was on holiday from school, was playing chess with a friend in the lounge.

I walked in to the lounge and said to them, 'Do you know where there are any matches?'

'There's a lighter over there.'

I picked it up and went upstairs to the guest room where I was sleeping until my own bedroom was ready.

Then I set fire to the curtains, dropped the lighter and ran out of the house.

\* \* \*

Still continuing with their game, Johnnie and his friend heard the front door slam. Then the carpenter rushed into the lounge and said, 'Where's your mother?'

'Why?'

'Nicola's set fire to the house again.'

The two boys ran upstairs, but all there was to see was a charred curtain, some scorching on the carpet and a small piece of damaged wallpaper. Johnnie shrugged. It didn't seem very important. Nicola had done so many things for so long he'd become immune to it all.

Meanwhile, the carpenter had found Pam in the office and was telling her how he'd seen smoke coming from under the door of the room that Nicola had been using. He'd rushed in and put out the fire with a bucket of water from the bathroom.

After inspecting the damage, Pam spoke to Sally and Johnnie before returning alone to the office. Where is all this going to end? she thought. She knew that if the workman hadn't been there, Nicola would have started a serious fire that could have injured or even killed her two other children. Certainly, working in the office, she couldn't have seen the fire and fires can take hold so quickly. 'This is getting ridiculous,' she said aloud. She picked up the telephone, dialled the number and, when someone answered, said, 'Is that the police?' Then she reported what Nicola had done.

Nicola was picked up at a neighbour's house and taken to the police station where she was charged with arson, endangering life and intent to kill her mother.

When Pam arrived at the police station, Nicola was being questioned.

Pam didn't know what to say to her daughter. She could only ask, 'Nicola, why did you do it again?'

Nicola looked at her blankly and Pam felt awful. There was nothing she could do to help her. She didn't know what Nicola was thinking. One minute, she hated her for what she had done and was terrified of her because, time and time again, Nicola had struck her, thrown knives at her and screamed obscenities at her. But the next minute, Nicola would be saying, 'Cuddle me, Mum.' So, although much of the time Nicola seemed to hate her mother, there were other times when her mother was the only one she wanted.

After the arrest formalities had been completed, Nicola was taken directly from the police station to Holloway Prison.

That evening, Pam knelt by her bed and in anguish prayed, 'Please, God, please let my daughter, Nicola, live a normal life again and I will never, never ask for anything else again.'

\*　　\*　　\*

When I was driven back into Holloway Prison, I believed that I was going to spend the rest of my life in an institution or secure establishment. It was a relief. Nobody would expect normal behaviour from someone who was institutionalized. The pressures of living would be mercifully lifted from my shoulders and there would be nothing to remind me of the past. Nobody would know that I was anything but an obese, ugly, mad woman.

I was again sent to C1, the psychiatric unit, which was full of new people. Some of them frightened me to death. At night, I put crinkly toilet paper all round my bed so, if any of them sneaked up on me, I'd hear them.

Each day, we followed the same routine. We were woken at half-past seven for breakfast at eight. The only variation in this meal was that we might be given a fried egg instead of a sausage. We were then unlocked to clean out our cell. Except at weekends, we went at ten to occupational therapy. Lunch was at half-past eleven. From twelve until two, we were locked in our cells. There was more occupational therapy between two and half-past three, at which time we were given tea. We were then locked in again until half-past five when what was called 'association' began. I usually had a bath at that time or watched television. We were generally locked in for the night at seven, at which time we were given supper – a slice of cake, a cheese roll or, as a special treat, a piece of hot bread pudding. Medication came round at about half nine and then we all went to sleep. But it was a routine that I enjoyed. Somehow, because of it, I was more able to cope with the day.

I also enjoyed being given so much filling food, even though I constantly spoke about going on a diet. I did actually cut down my intake for a while when I was put on a scale and discovered that I was ten stone eight pounds, which was two stone overweight. But I didn't stick to my diet for long. What else was there to do but eat and who cared what I looked like?

Within a short time of being in Holloway, I began to be visited by various specialists who'd been brought in to see if they could find out what was wrong with me. The prison doctor told me that the drugs I'd been given by Dr Goble were extremely strong and might have had some unpleasant side-effects and could have strained my whole system. I was well aware that for months I'd been totally switched off from reality. But it was still felt that I needed to be calmed down, and so they tried out different drugs on me. However, I knew that when my feelings returned, I would crack. What I couldn't imagine was how drastically I would be affected by the return to reality.

\*     \*     \*

168

With Nicola back in Holloway so quickly after her trial, Ed and Pam were bitter, angry and confused. Their visits to her became increasingly strained and they both felt that they were losing contact with her. She was growing distant from them. They couldn't put their finger on the cause, but there was an obvious tension between them. She was always pleased to see them, but there were things that perhaps all of them ought to have said, but no-one knew how to put into words.

Both Pam and Ed were convinced that Nicola was a seriously sick girl. They were also convinced that the psychiatric treatment she'd received had been a failure and they no longer believed in this approach. But they knew of no alternative and so they had nothing positive to say to Nicola. Because they also did not know where to turn, they felt they were in a period of limbo. Friends were again supportive and sympathetic, but they needed to speak to professional people who could help and advise them.

Mr Smythe, their solicitor, was extremely helpful and he immediately snapped into action, discussing possible strategies with Ed in meetings and over the phone. Mr Smythe decided to instruct Dr Morley to visit Nicola in Holloway again so that he and Mr Giacomo, the barrister, could decide upon the basis for the defence. But nothing could be done for a few weeks because, as it was the middle of August, both Mr Smythe and Dr Morley were about to go abroad on their summer holidays.

Ed also discussed Nicola with the prison doctor, who suggested that she was likely to need hospital care for a long period. He gave Ed the addresses of several possible private clinics. It sounded hopeful but, when Ed began telephoning the doctors in charge of these special clinics, he rapidly realized that finding a placement for Nicola was not going to be easy. Some of the clinics were non-residential, others could only take people from a certain area and most dealt solely with minors or adolescents and, as Nicola was now over eighteen, she was legally an adult. With no possibility of bail being granted, it was clear that, for the time being at least, Nicola would have to stay in Holloway.

★    ★    ★

Every day, I had visitors. Either Mum came herself or arranged for a friend or relative to call. It was something to look forward to. For a long time, Sally wasn't able to come to the prison because she was at school during the week and on Saturday mornings she went to the Royal Academy of Music. But, almost six weeks after I'd been sent to Holloway, it was arranged that she could visit on a Saturday afternoon, a time usually reserved for visits to convicted prisoners.

Although I knew I was unattractively fat, I made an effort to look presentable. To give my face a little colour, I even attempted to put on some make-up, using the bottom of an Ajax tin as a mirror.

We greeted each other in the visiting hall as warmly as we could and, for a time, my father took a back seat, perhaps hoping that Sally, who was naturally optimistic and encouraging, would lift my spirits. But, as we sat there, she was holding my hand so tightly that I could feel her whole body trembling, despite the regulation table that separated us.

I knew it was a difficult visit for them both. Almost as if I were a spectator, I listened to my father's progress report. Applications had been made to several hospitals to find me a place, and they were awaiting replies. If I was accepted by any of them, I'd almost certainly start to improve under the excellent supervision and treatment that would be provided. No, the last specialist report hadn't clearly indicated what was wrong, but it wouldn't be too long before somebody was found who could help.

Poor Dad failed to realize that I could see the desperation in his eyes and could easily detect the false cheerfulness in his voice. He looked exhausted. Apart from the huge black circles that shadowed his eyes, his face was ashen.

As usual, the thirty minutes of visiting time flew by. Sally leant across the table and we embraced each other. As we parted, I could see that, though she was smiling, tears were welling up in her large blue eyes.

My father stepped forward and, although the regulations forbade such close physical contact, clasped the back of my head and pulled me to him.

'It won't be long, darling,' he declared. 'Just a few more weeks – I promise. Everything's under control.' For a brief moment, he looked into my eyes and then fleetingly kissed the top of my head and my temple.

'I know you and Mum are doing everything you can,' I said.

'And we'll succeed, Nicola,' he said determinedly. 'Mark my words. I promise you.'

He smiled and said his cheerful farewells, but I knew these masked the misery and fear he really felt.

I was escorted away into a small room nearby where I was searched before being returned to my cell. Ignoring the three other prisoners I was currently sharing with, I sat down on my bed and stared out of the barred window at the endless red-brick walls. From almost every window, girls and women were hurling abuse, screaming hysterically or making filthy suggestions to the girls they fancied.

'Have you got a roll-up, Nicky?'

I was startled by the quiet Irish voice and turned to face Maria, who obviously knew that I'd just had visitors. Her hair, as always, was matted and dirty. On her chin were two brown moles with hairs sprouting from them. Her few remaining teeth were stained yellow with the tobacco she greedily smoked. Because she stood so close, the stale odour of her unwashed body filled my nostrils. But what really frightened me were her eyes – brilliant blue, piercing eyes, edged with thick black lashes. It was uncanny that such an ugly woman could possess such beautiful eyes.

'Maria, you know I don't smoke. I've told you a hundred times. Please, just leave me alone.'

I fought to keep my voice calm, but she always made me nervous. I'd seen enough of her violent tempers to realize her total lack of control and terrifying physical strength.

She gave me a long hard look and then shuffled over to her bed. Revolting woman! I couldn't bear it any more. Hateful fucking world! I cursed to myself. Fucking awful people! Useless doctors. What do they know? Not a fucking thing!

The place, the people, they ground on my nerves.

The next moment, my whole body froze and a high-pitched scream echoed around the room. My scream. I saw a hand, my hand, pick up a glass bottle of moisturizing cream and smash it repeatedly against the unbreakable window. Thousands of particles of glass rocketed through the air and a mass of warm blood seeped slowly down my uplifted arm.

An alarm bell sounded, almost immediately followed by the clatter of heavy running in the echoing corridor. Nearby, a voice – Maria's voice – kept repeating, 'Jesus Christ! Holy Mother of God! Jesus Christ! Holy Mother of God!'

I still had a large piece of glass in my left hand and I thrust it repeatedly into my right palm, viciously digging it deeper every time. Four big women in blue had now entered the cell, boxing me in. I jumped on to my bed and started to lash out at them, the piece of glass still in my hand. 'Get away, you fucking screws!' I screamed. 'Let me finish!' I was crying so hard that it was impossible to focus my eyes and see what I was doing. In a last desperate attempt to kill myself, I clasped my left hand and the broken glass to my throat.

Two pairs of hands grabbed me and threw me face down on the bed. A vice-like grip encircled my ankles. My face was pushed roughly down into the bedclothes, making it difficult to breathe. I screamed and screamed as I felt my dress being thrown up and my pants being pulled down to my knees. I caught my breath as a sharp pain shot through me, quickly followed by a feeling of exhaustion.

'That should calm her down a bit,' said a disembodied voice.

I was turned over and found myself staring into the face of a black nurse.

'Now, Nicola,' she said calmly, 'let's take a look at that hand.'

\* \* \*

That Saturday evening, Ed and Pam had settled comfortably into the armchairs in the sitting-room. Earlier, they'd spent an hour or so in the garden, tidying up dead leaves already shed by some of the shrubs and smaller trees. The work had been soothingly therapeutic and, at least for a while, they'd been able to think about something other than Nicola. But now, washed and refreshed with mugs of tea, they wanted to discuss what was happening and in particular to listen to Sally's reactions upon seeing her sister.

It was a subject that Sally would have preferred not to discuss, not because she was afraid of further upsetting her parents, but because she was herself confused. Although she loved her sister and was desperately concerned about her plight, she couldn't suppress the feeling that, although things were now out of control, Nicola had set out to draw attention to herself and had at least succeeded in absorbing all her parents' energies at a time when she needed their help with her own emotional problems.

For a long time she was able to keep out of her parents' way, because she was getting ready to go out to a disco. But at last she came into the sitting-room, resplendent in her soft flowing dress and high-heeled shoes. Both father and mother smiled appreciatively at their beautiful daughter. Sally stood just inside the door, knowing that at any moment her boyfriend would be calling for her.

Looking directly at her, Pam said, 'How did Nicola seem to you this afternoon?'

Sally answered immediately, 'I think they're looking after her very well. Of course, she's overweight, but she looked fit.'

She paused, hoping her parents would settle for that. She had at least been able to say something positive. In fact, she'd been surprised at Nicola's apparently healthy complexion. She'd expected her to look grey or pallid, locked away as she was from the sun and fresh air. But other things had changed. Their conversation had been strained and stilted. She could no longer reach her sister who in some strange way seemed remote and separate, unwilling to respond to human contact. But that was not something she wanted to say to her parents. They needed to be reassured that all was well.

So, without further prompting, Sally added, 'Nicola's always been a bit of an actress – I suppose she had to be for her dancing. She's really so good at it that it's difficult for me to tell whether she's acting or not. But she doesn't seem that much different to me now from the way she's always been.'

Pam smiled and Ed nodded approvingly. The doorbell announced the arrival of Sally's boyfriend and with a cheerful, 'Bye. See you later,' she was off, though not before her father had put in his usual, 'Don't be late, Sally!'

Ed gave his wife a cautious gin and ample tonic, concerned about her mixing alcohol with the daily Valium tablets she was taking. In contrast, he poured himself a generous whisky with a touch of ginger ale. They sipped their drinks in silence. Their reverie was abruptly halted when the telephone rang.

'Ed Owen speaking.'

'Mr Owen, this is Wardress Benson of the Medical Unit, Holloway Prison . . .'

Ed was immediately stricken with fear. Seeing this on his face, Pam hurried from her chair to stand close to the telephone so that she too could hear what was being said.

'What's the matter?' Ed demanded anxiously.

'Your daughter, Nicola, attempted suicide tonight and cut through the main tendon in her right wrist with broken glass.' Both Pam and Ed had braced themselves for an expected blow, but when it came its impact was shattering. 'She was taken to hospital,' Wardress Benson continued unemotionally, 'and the external wound has been stitched, but she'll need to have an operation to fully repair the damage. The surgeon who saw her said the operation will take place in two or three days' time.'

'Is she all right?' Ed asked, his voice calm, his anguish concealed, but his mind in turmoil. 'Can my wife and I come now to see her?'

'I'm afraid not. Nicola has committed a serious breach of prison regulations. So she has to forgo certain privileges. One of these is that she will not be allowed visitors for a while. But I can assure you she's quite all right and is being well cared for.'

Ed had a great deal of respect for the staff of Holloway and admired their no-nonsense approach. He knew that their prompt action had probably saved Nicola's life. So he saw no point in making unreasonable demands or trying to get the decision revoked. 'Thank you for telling us,' he said quietly. 'Is there anything else?'

'No, nothing,' the wardress replied. 'I'll let you know if there are any further developments.'

By the time Ed had replaced the receiver, Pam had slumped sideways in her chair, her head resting on the arm. Her whole body was shaking with her silent sobbing. Ed moved across to her and for a few moments, they held each other tightly in mutual support.

Then, in anguish, Pam cried, 'I want to see her! She's my baby. Why won't they let me see her?'

Ed couldn't answer her question and they lapsed again into silence. Through both their minds ran the fears of further dangers that might beset Nicola – problems with the operation, the possibility of permanent damage, even of paralysis. With Nicola no longer in their care and out of reach, they felt helpless, bemused, distraught. There had to be something they could do to help.

'Phone Dr Sangster, Ed,' Pam said. 'I want to make sure they're doing the right thing.'

With something concrete to do, Ed sprang into action.

Faced with another example of Nicola's alarming caprice, Dr Sangster, the kind and considerate hospital consultant who'd previously treated Nicola, did his best to help. 'I've a friend who's a top surgeon,' he said reassuringly. 'Almost certainly he'll know the surgeon who saw Nicola this evening. Let me see if I can get hold of him. Then I'll get back to you – hopefully with some answers.'

Fifteen minutes later, Dr Sangster rang back. He confirmed that everything necessary had been done for Nicola and explained why the operation had been delayed for a couple of days. Ed thanked the doctor for his help. There was nothing left to do but wait.

\* \* \*

I was taken to hospital and my hand was stitched. I was told that this was a temporary measure. Because I'd badly damaged the main tendon, an operation was necessary, but arrangements had first to be made with the prison governor.

Having been driven back to Holloway, I was marched along the corridors. To my astonishment I was dragged past my own cell. It took me less than a second to realize where they were taking me. I tried to pull away. 'You can't put me in there!' I screamed. 'I can't take it! No, miss, I promise I'll be good. Please, don't! Please!'

It took three wardresses to drag me into that room and I had to be given another injection before they could put me into a strip dress and leave me in the solitary confinement of the strip cell. The window was shuttered. There was no bed, no light – nothing, except a mattress and a plastic potty. The shapeless dress was stiff and unbearable and irritated my skin. I snatched up the potty and started to crash it repeatedly against the door. I banged, swore and raved for hours. But nobody came. Finally, exhausted, I collapsed on to the mattress.

This was the start of the loneliest weeks of my life.

# CHAPTER FIFTEEN

## *Disposal Broadmoor*

It was completely dark in the strip cell. All visits were stopped and I didn't see anybody. Like a crazed, caged animal, I was fed through the hatch in the door. It was only from the pattern of meal times that I knew whether it was night or day.

Unexpectedly, after three days, there was a jangling of keys and my cell door was unlocked. Then, under police guard, I was taken from the prison back to the hospital for an operation on my hand. Astonishingly, it appeared to be in the middle of the night.

As soon as I started to come round from the anaesthetic, I was rushed out of the hospital and escorted back to Holloway and locked again in the strip cell. My hand was terribly painful and throbbed all the time. I also developed a raging thirst and kept on shouting for a glass of water.

'Be quiet!' the wardress shouted back. 'You're not allowed any water. Be quiet!'

As I lay sobbing in agony on the unwelcoming mattress, I thought, Can anybody get lower than I am?

\*   \*   \*

With Nicola back in Holloway, the Owens slowly returned to a semblance of normal family life. Ed and Pam started to go out again. They went to a weekly jazz club and started playing squash. All too aware of how much time and energy they had been spending on Nicola, they also deliberately spent as much time as they could with Sally and Johnnie.

As Johnnie was away at boarding-school, he only came home during the holidays and for odd weekends. Because of this, in the previous months, he'd seen far less of Nicola's disruptive behaviour than the other members of the family. But he still was affected by it. He'd seen the grief that Nicola had already inflicted on his parents and was determined to do nothing that might add to it. So he couldn't be a rebel. He felt he couldn't even properly be himself. It was a heavy responsibility for a thirteen year old.

With Nicola's future seeming so grim, Johnnie became concerned about her for the first time. There was nobody to console or reassure him at boarding-school but he found great comfort in talking to God and spent a lot of time praying.

He also started to have vivid dreams about Nicola. In one that often recurred, his sister was in a cemetery, tied to a cross above a grave. Although she was weeping, she said, 'I'm being helped now. I'm going to get better.' He could see that she was in pain and so he desperately tried, but failed, to untie her from the cross as it sank slowly into the ground, taking Nicola away. When she'd disappeared, he stood back from the grave and saw that in front of it were the massive stone numbers '25'. This dream, Johnnie assumed, meant that God had intervened and that good would triumph so that when Nicola was twenty–five she really would be better.

Sally, too, first became really concerned about her sister at this time, even though she had personal problems of her own. Although extremely talented, she was by nature temperamental and not disposed to work unnecessarily hard. As attention had been centred on Nicola throughout the year, Sally had not concentrated sufficiently on her academic studies and her O level results had been disappointing. She stayed on at school to retake some of the examinations and start her A level courses, but her heart wasn't in the work. Her music studies too were not going as well as once they had. For one who had always found it easy to make friends, she felt strangely lonely and to her own surprise realized that she actually missed her elder sister and wanted her back home. Cushioned by her parents from the frightening realities of the situation, Sally felt sure that eventually everything was going to be all right for Nicola.

Despite his frequent shows of bravado, Ed was less certain. Although determined to achieve what was best for Nicola, he hadn't as yet discovered exactly what that was. As a result, he was inclined to lash out wildly at what he took to be the incompetence and conspiratorial secrecy of at least some members of the medical and legal professions.

Superficially at least, Pam was much calmer. But she was racked by inner doubts and an unquenchable feeling of guilt. So many doctors, psychiatrists, policemen, probation officers and lawyers had delved into the possible causes of Nicola's behaviour that she couldn't help constantly asking herself, Am I to blame? She was all too aware that, with Ed so often away, it had been she who'd so incensed Nicola by regularly checking her room. It had been she who'd taken Nicola to the hospital for the weekly injections of tranquillizers that had turned her daughter into a walking automaton. It had been she who'd rung the police to report the second arson and so it was because of her that Nicola was in Holloway. But, although Pam could barely admit it to herself, she felt a great sense of relief that Nicola was no longer at home. The tension she'd generated when she was there was slowly dispersing and Pam felt hopeful that while Nicola was in prison somebody, somewhere, might be able to find out what was wrong with her. That was something she and Ed certainly hadn't been able to do.

*          *          *

After spending a week in the strip cell, my own clothes were returned and I was allowed to change out of the strip dress. Half an hour later, I took off my tights, tied them tightly round my neck and was trying desperately to strangle myself when a wardress rushed in to prevent me. As a punishment, all my clothes were taken away from me, even my strip dress, and I was left naked.

When next I was fed through the hatch, I hurled the cup of boiling tea at the wardress's face. As they'd taken away all my clothes and stopped my visits, there was nothing more they could do to me. I was being treated like a wild animal and so I behaved like one.

*          *          *

Pam picked up the phone as soon as it rang. In constant dread of receiving bad news from the prison, she was relieved to hear it was Mr Smythe, the solicitor handling Nicola's case.

'I wanted to speak to you, Mrs Owen,' he said, 'because Mr Owen doesn't seem in the right frame of mind to discuss such matters at the moment.'

Pamela smiled ruefully. 'What can I do to help?' she asked.

'Well, first of all, I wanted to report that a Dr Boardman, who is the medical director of a hospital that could possibly assist Nicola, has agreed to see her in the next couple of days. Of course, I don't want to raise your hopes unduly.'

'Thank you. Let's hope he'll be able to give us some good news.'

'Indeed, although I have to report that I've also spoken at some length to Dr Morley. You'll recall that the report he wrote the last time she was in prison impressed the judge when Nicola was tried for arson at the Old Bailey. I'm sure the report was instrumental in achieving such a satisfactory outcome. Well, I asked him to revisit Nicola, which he has now done. Both he and Dr Wells, the chief psychiatrist at Holloway Prison, concur that it is going to be exceptionally difficult to find a suitable placement for Nicola. As you know, many of the places that might have been suitable will take only adolescents and, unfortunately, Nicola is now eighteen. Moreover, she is a double arsonist and hospital authorities have to think very seriously about accepting somebody who is potentially a danger to the other patients. Perhaps Dr Boardman may be willing to help but, meanwhile, Dr Morley would like you and Mr Owen to visit him at his home so that he can put his conclusion to you personally.'

Pam had listened carefully and instinctively felt deeply concerned. 'Is it bad news?' she asked.

'I can assure you, Mrs Owen, that everybody, myself included, is doing everything we can to help Nicola.'

Although aware that this was not an adequate answer to her question, Pam knew it was useless to press him further and so she asked, 'When would Dr Morley like us to visit him?'

'He suggests you call at 10 a.m. on Thursday, 21 September. Will that be convenient for you and Mr Owen?'

Pam first checked Ed's office diary and then said, 'Yes, we can both manage the twenty-first.'

'Thank you, Mrs Owen. I'll drop you a line confirming the appointment and giving you Dr Morley's home address.'

After the polite farewells, Pam put down the phone. Mr Smythe had been kind and reassuring, but there was something about his call that she found disturbing.

\*    \*    \*

182

Eventually, I was briefly released from solitary confinement in the strip cell so that I could have a bath. I was tense with determination as I stepped into the bath. My moment came when the two wardresses had turned away, I quickly slipped down in the bath so that my head was immersed in the tepid water. When their brawny hands suddenly grabbed me and tried to pull me out, I fought like a demon. Why wouldn't they let me drown? What point was there in keeping me alive?

\*     \*     \*

When Ed and Pam arrived at Dr Morley's apartment, a Spanish maid ushered them into a spacious sitting-room. After she'd told them that the doctor would join them shortly, she offered to bring them refreshments and invited them to sit in a pair of commodious armchairs. A few minutes later, Dr Morley joined them and, while they drank their coffee, told them how he'd come by the brightly-coloured, Hungarian cushions which Pam so much admired.

It was only after the coffee cups had been taken away that Dr Morley began to discuss Nicola's case. He was obviously an understanding and compassionate man who was determined to provide Ed and Pam with as much help and support as he could. He chose his words carefully.

Having said that it was most unlikely that a secure hospital in the private sector could be found that would accept Nicola, a double arsonist, he went on, 'You've got three children, Mr and Mrs Owen. Two of them are perfect and two out of three isn't bad. I suggest, therefore, that you concentrate your lives around your two other children because, in my opinion, it is unlikely that Nicola will ever get well. Her unpredictable, irrational and maniacal behaviour adds up to a very seriously disturbed young person. That is why, having spoken to Dr Wells, the prison psychiatrist, I concur with his view that should a suitable hospital refuse her admission, as it may well do, then as a last resort Broadmoor must be considered.'

At these words, Pam and Ed froze with horror. Dr Morley too remained silent and still, his eyes staring fixedly at the intricate pattern of a Persian rug.

Ed was the first to speak. 'Dr Morley,' he said, 'in plain English you're telling my wife and I that our daughter, Nicola, is incurably mad?'

Dr Morley grimaced and lifted his hand in half-hearted protest at such unprofessional language before saying, 'It is a most unfortunate situation, but I have discussed the matter with both Dr Wells and also with Dr Boardman, the medical director of a secure hospital, who has seen your daughter. Regretfully, I have to tell you that we are all agreed as to the prognosis.'

'Dr Morley,' Ed continued, 'we had a lovely daughter until she was fourteen and there were no emotional problems. She was a little weak as a child and suffered more than her fair share of childhood illnesses. Dancing strengthened her and considerably so. Until these awful events took over she was on course for a professional dancing career. My wife and I cannot understand what has happened and I must tell you we cannot come to terms with it.'

Patiently, Dr Morley replied, 'It is most unfortunate, a tragedy in fact.' It was clear that these were meant to be his final words. There was nothing more he felt he could say.

But Ed had not finished. 'Where does madness come from, Dr Morley?' he said in a low even voice.

'You cannot ask me that.'

'I just have. If we're to come to terms with this, somebody, somewhere, has to give an answer. Does madness come out of the ground, out of the sky, or is it some virus floating in the air? Nicola has had complete medical examinations and nothing connects. At fourteen, she is a lovely and perfectly sane young girl. At eighteen, she is being declared insane and, if I've understood you correctly, there's a high probability that she is incurably insane. I just don't understand it.'

'Mr Owen,' the doctor protested, 'I say again, you cannot ask me that.'

'I'm sorry,' Ed persisted, 'but what I'm asking is whether you can suggest, even speculatively, some factor or factors that, in your opinion, could cause madness in a young girl who has had no previous history of mental disorder and whose general physical health was good.'

Like Ed, Pam hadn't taken her eyes off Dr Morley. She had often been irritated by Ed's habit of pushing for a logical explanation of everything but, in this case, where the future of the daughter they both loved was at stake, she wanted an answer as much as her husband. From out of her handbag, she pulled a colour photograph mounted on white card. As she passed it to Dr Morley, she said softly, 'This was my daughter.'

Dr Morley gazed at the photograph of a smiling and graceful Nicola dressed in one of the national dance costumes that Pam had made – a lace pill-box hat with two thick lace strands hanging from the back, a tightly fitted, short, green-velvet jacket with a frill at the waist trimmed with bright red braid, a swirling black pleated skirt, a white lace apron, and a pair of red leather anklet boots. Also in the photograph was a small table on which stood the five silver cups that Nicola had won for the dance.

'That is the Nicola you have never seen,' Pam continued. 'Our Nicola . . . our . . . ' For a moment, she had to force back her tears. 'You see, Dr Morley, why we can't accept your conclusion? That photograph was taken only four years ago.'

Dr Morley said nothing but handed back the photograph which Pam returned immediately to her handbag.

Looking up, Pam said to him, 'She was all right until she started her periods.'

Once again, Ed and Pam stared intently at him, willing him to speak, willing him to say something that would give them even a ray of hope.

It was only after some moments' deliberation that Dr Morley decided to speculate aloud. 'It is possible,' he said quietly, 'that there is something already present that emerges with the onset of puberty. It may be so in Nicola's case but I don't know. I think that she may have two illnesses. One that I am sure about is an emotional illness that I suspect is not severe, although, given the possibility of the second illness, it is difficult for me to assess. I believe, however, that this first illness, if it really is the first of two illnesses, would almost certainly be susceptible to treatment and possibly a treatment of a not extended nature.' Then he paused.

'And the other illness?' Pam prompted.

Looking directly at her, he said, 'I am not at all sure what the other illness is but I am sure that it is present. I am not sure of its severity, but I am inclined to believe that it could be the major factor.' Once again, there was silence. Then, after much consideration, Dr Morley announced, 'I suspect the endocrine.'

Ed and Pam looked at each other blankly. Both had hoped that the mystery was about to be unravelled but, for the time being at least, that hadn't happened. Neither Pam nor Ed had the faintest idea what the endocrine was. So bemused and dispirited were they by this time that they didn't even think of asking.

After they'd left Dr Morley's apartment, Ed and Pam paused outside in the gardens for a while and in silence watched the countless colourful fish swimming among the water lilies in the ornamental pond. Holding each other's hand for comfort, neither of them spoke for some minutes.

Then Pam looked up at her husband and said, 'Poor, poor Nicola. It's so frightening. You never hear of people coming out of Broadmoor, do you? Eddie, I don't believe there isn't a doctor somewhere who can't cure our Nicola.'

Ed looked down at his petite and pretty wife. During the last few traumatic months she had lost quite a lot of weight and looked extremely elegant in her tailored white suit. He squeezed her hand and, even managing a weak smile, said, 'Pamsie, you're right. We're going to keep on fighting for our Nicola.' It was a positive, hopeful note to follow what had been a dirge of sadness and despair.

'Dr Morley is a good man and I don't think he's so sure about Nicola,' Pam said.

Ed nodded slowly. 'I hope I didn't offend him.'

'Oh, he understands. He must see situations like ours every day.'

'Well, not every day, I hope, or there wouldn't be any places left in Holloway!'

Pam smiled briefly and then said determinedly, 'Eddie, I want to see Nicola. I really do. I really—'

'I do too. But you know that at the moment she's not allowed to have visitors.'

'I know, but—'

'All right, let's go. I'm sure we'll think of some way of managing it between us. Come on. Let's go to see our Nicola.'

After a long drive through unfamiliar London suburbs, they managed to arrive at the prison during the official visiting period. A pleasant, young wardress led them from the visitors' reception area to the medical unit. As they passed through an open area in front of a cell block, a young woman screamed down at them, 'You down there, you think you've got it made. Well, you're nothing – that's what you are, fucking nothing.'

'That poor girl,' the wardress said, 'she'd only been out of here three weeks and they'd got her back on drugs. She's only a kid. The only really safe place for her is in prison. Drug pushers should be hanged. They destroy so many people's lives.' She suddenly stopped and looked at them. 'I shouldn't have said that,' she said, 'but in this place you see so many ruined lives. It breaks your heart sometimes.'

'Well, if it wasn't for the staff at Holloway,' Pam said thoughtfully, 'our daughter wouldn't be alive today. We think you do a marvellous job and we're grateful.'

They'd arrived at the medical unit and, after unlocking and relocking the multitudinous doors, the wardress led them into the supervisor's office.

A most pleasant, robust young woman squeezed round her desk to greet them. 'Hello,' she said. 'I'm Jean Harrison, the Medical Supervisor.' When Ed and Pam were seated, she went on, 'I was delighted when reception rang to tell me you were here. I've been wanting to talk about your daughter.'

'Oh, yes,' Pam said. 'We know all about it. We've just come from Dr Morley and he's told us that it's been recommended that Nicola is sent to Broadmoor.'

Mrs Harrison smiled and she replied, 'Mrs Owen, I'll tell you this: it's easier to go to heaven than it is to Broadmoor. Anyway, I'm informed that Nicola's been giving us a bad time at the moment. On Sunday evening, she tried to drown herself in the bath. Fortunately, the officers caught her in time, although Nicola then started to attack them.' Seeing the looks of horror on Ed's and Pam's faces, Mrs Harrison smiled again and added, 'Don't worry, the officers were only slightly hurt, although one of the girls' watches was smashed in the fracas.'

'We'll pay for that, of course,' Ed said.

'Thank you, Mr Owen, but that won't be necessary. The loss will be covered by the authority. I must say, Mr and Mrs Owen, that your daughter appears to have an amazingly strong will.'

'I know,' Ed said. 'And I want you to know that my wife and I are very appreciative of everything you are doing for Nicola.'

Again Mrs Harrison smiled. 'We are not going to give up on Nicola,' she said. 'You may not believe this, but we've had worse cases than Nicola's and they have walked out of the strip cell and out of Holloway Prison. And they haven't gone to Broadmoor either!' She glanced down at the file in front of her before continuing. 'I see from these notes that you have referred to Nicola's mood swings and her periods. That's very interesting. While she remains with us in the medical unit, I think I'll see if we can make some record of her menstrual cycle. It might give a few pointers.'

'But both Dr Wells and Dr Morley seem to have already made up their minds,' Pam said. 'And they're apparently of the same opinion.'

'And what might that be?' she asked while carefully reading something in the file that had attracted her attention.

'That Nicola's mad,' Pam said disconsolately.

Mrs Harrison looked up. 'They're both very experienced psychiatrists,' she said. 'They also both happen to be men.' She put the file down and said, 'I have a note here from Dr Wells about a change that he intends to start making tomorrow to Nicola's medication. Let's hope it brings about an improvement. Now, as you know, Nicola has, for the moment, lost her entitlement to visitors and I appreciate it that you have not asked to see her. If she behaves, it will be possible for her to have a visit on Saturday and so you will be able to spend some time with her then.' She stood up and added, conspiratorially, 'But I am sure we are not breaking the rules if you just have a quick word with her now. Would you like to?'

Speechless with delight, Ed and Pam nodded their head vigorously.

Mrs Harrison led them a short distance down the corridor before stopping in front of a heavy wooden door. With a gesture she indicated that this was Nicola's strip cell.

Ed stepped forward and stooped down so that he could look through a narrow slit set in the door. At first, he

189

could only see the back of his daughter's head and her shoulders. He tried to reposition himself, hoping to see more of her but he couldn't.

Forcing himself to stop his voice wavering, he said gently, 'Nicola, it's Dad.'

She turned her head to look directly at the door. 'Dad, is that you?'

'It's me, Nicola.'

She cried out with despair and misery, 'Dad, Dad. Oh, it really is you.' Rushing to the door, she tried moving her head from side to side in an effort to see more of him through the narrow slit. As she saw his face, her eyes filled with tears and she began to cry, 'Dad! Oh my Dad! Dad!'

'Nicola, listen, my darling!' Ed said, desperate not to add to his daughter's misery. 'I've come to tell you we're making a lot of progress and things are really starting to happen.'

'Dad, please get me out of here! Please, Dad, tell them I won't be any more trouble.' It was a half-strangled, sobbing plea.

Ed wanted to hold, to comfort his daughter, but he only had words. 'Be brave, my darling. Be brave for Mum. Be brave for me. We'll soon have you out of here.' He glanced at Pam standing next to the medical supervisor and out of Nicola's sight. Her eyes begged him not to let Nicola know she was there. The agony of the situation had drained her.

'Get me out of here,' Nicola wept. 'Dad, Dad, get me out of here.'

'Nicola, please try for us. We love you so much and think about you every minute of the day.'

Just then, as Ed felt he was about to break down, Mrs Harrison stepped forward and gently pushed him to one side. To Nicola she said, 'Your father has to go now, Nicola, to see the doctor.'

'Don't go, Dad! Stay with me!' she screamed.

Ed's throat was completely dry. He couldn't utter another word. Looking through the slit in the door at the tear-filled eyes of his daughter, he kissed the top of his fingers and held them out in front of his face. Then, as the tears flowed down his cheeks, he turned away.

*     *     *

It was the worst moment in my life. I can't remember what Dad said. I remember only his eyes looking at me through the slit in the strip-cell door. I shall never forget the despair in those eyes. It still comes back to haunt me because I've never seen anybody else look so devastated.

# CHAPTER SIXTEEN

## *The Search Begins*

Cheerful as usual, Sally opened the front door for her parents as they returned from their visit to Dr Morley and the trauma of seeing Nicola in the strip cell. Their long, weary faces told her that something was wrong.

'What's the matter?' she asked, as Ed and Pam walked into the lobby.

'What's the matter!' Pam snapped. 'Nothing's the matter except your sister is stuck in a strip cell, she keeps on trying to kill herself and all the doctors think she's incurably mad!'

'All right, Mum. You don't have to be cross with me,' Sally replied patiently. 'What did Dr Morley say?'

'He said that Nicola was probably born with something wrong with her and the only place for her to go is Broadmoor.'

'Broadmoor! That's awful, isn't it?'

'Well, it's not another prison. It's a secure hospital for people they term criminally insane. Oh, dear Sally,' Pam said, putting an arm around her, 'it's a good job I've got you. What are we going to do?'

Waiting for a more detailed explanation of the day's events, Sally followed her parents into the sitting-room and curled up in an armchair as Ed poured a couple of stiff drinks for himself and Pam. To Sally's surprise, her dad also offered her a Martini. Sensing that the seriousness of the occasion warranted it, she accepted.

Obviously feeling that it was necessary to lighten the general atmosphere of gloom, Pam started by giving Sally an account of what Jean Harrison, the supervisor of the medical unit at Holloway, had said, adding, 'I'm not sure but I rather gathered that she's on our side. She said she was going to keep a check on Nicola's periods and she made some cryptic comment about men doctors not always understanding.' Then, suddenly unable to conceal any longer her own fears and sense of foreboding, Pam burst into tears, and sobbed, 'Poor Nicola. She'd be better off dead than locked away for the rest of her life in Broadmoor!'

'Don't you ever say that again. Never! Do you hear me?' Ed shouted at his wife.

In the silence that followed, tears ran down Pam's face and Ed slumped back in his armchair, balancing his whisky glass on his stomach.

After a while, as Ed continued to gaze at the ceiling, he said, 'What is a bloody endocrine?'

Neither Pam nor Sally replied. They didn't know either.

'I've got an idea, Pam,' Ed said. 'My cousin Mo wants to see Nicola so why don't you take her along on Saturday? I feel sure I can be more use to Nicola by taking myself off to the public library.'

The voyage of discovery was about to begin.

Two days later, early on Saturday morning, Ed arrived at Bexleyheath Public Library. He was vaguely concerned that he might not be able to find sufficient information there and wondered if it might not have been more sensible for him to track down a specialist library in London. But he consoled himself with the thought that he had to start somewhere.

Well prepared for his research, he carried a thick pad of lined foolscap paper and an assortment of pens were stuffed into the inside pocket of his jacket. Having tracked down the section of medical books, he scanned the shelves. There was only one word he was looking for, 'Endocrine', and he assumed that it was of such medical significance that there would be a large and impressive tome standing there with an obvious title such as *The Human Endocrine*, *The Endocrine Gland* or even *The Endocrine System*. A quick glance showed him that there was no such book.

He was about to ask for help from one of the librarians silently working behind the counter, when he thought, I'm pathetic. Even a schoolkid could make a start at this.

Looking back at the rows of books, his eye was caught by the *Dictionary of Medical Terms*. He took this off the shelf and placed it on the floor. Continuing his search, he seized upon the *Companion to Medicine* in two substantial volumes. Finally, he selected a large medical dictionary. With the foolscap paper gripped firmly between his teeth, he gathered up his four weighty tomes and made his way to an empty chair at a table by the window.

Always a methodical man, Ed carefully placed the books to the left of the table, the pad of writing-paper in the centre and, to the right, the collection of pens which he thoughtfully wedged between his stiff pocket notebook and his diary to stop them rolling off in all directions.

He began with the *Dictionary of Medical Terms*. Having looked up 'Endocrine', he started making notes on his pad in capital letters. When he finished reading the entry, he looked through his notes and summarized them: 'The endocrine system produces in the body chemicals that are called hormones.'

Next, he looked up 'Hormones' and, as he read, he noted down the key words – ovaries, secretions, body metabolic rate, menstruation. The first and last of these words seemed so important that he underlined them. He looked up several other entries in the dictionary but found nothing that he though was relevant.

He decided to switch to the *Companion to Medicine*. He had some difficulty with this until he realized that the index to both volumes was at the end of the second one. With the aid of this, he located and read all the references to the endocrine. In his notebook, he listed the most important glands in the system – pituitary, thyroid, parathyroid, adrenal, pancreas. Then he moved on to *Endocrinology – The Study of the Endocrine Glands*. In this he learnt that in 1775 a man named Pott had removed the herniated ovaries from a young woman who had ceased to menstruate. He also read, with a smile, that it was a man named Owen who in 1852 had first noted animal parathyroid glands.

All this had taken several hours and so Ed stood up, stretched his legs and walked across to a young librarian. 'I'm just going out for half an hour,' he said to her. 'Could you kindly keep an eye on my little work area over there.'

She looked at him unsmilingly and somewhat disapprovingly said, 'We provide a public service here and you are not entitled to reserve a place at a table during your absence in case it is needed by another member of the public.'

'Well, I'm very sorry,' Ed replied, 'but I'm in desperate need of a public service which you don't seem to provide.'

With that he hurried out of the building and made his way to the public toilet in the nearby car park. Taking the opportunity to check that his car was safe, he was distressed to see that it was in desperate need of a wash down and polish.

Drawing heavily on a much-needed cigarette, he mulled over what he had read. Much of it meant nothing to him and he was beginning to feel that he wasn't going to discover anything, but going through his mind were four words which seemed to have constantly recurred – endocrine, ovaries, hormones, menstruation. Determined to plough on, he returned to the library. He was pleased to discover that nobody had invaded his territory.

Following up the cross-references, Ed looked up 'Hypothalamus'. He glanced through the long article and had almost come to the end when he was brought up with a start. 'Pituitary deficiency,' it said, 'has long been suspected in anorexia nervosa and evidence suggests that the endocrine disturbance of this disorder is of hypothalamus origin.'

This, at last, was something that might be directly connected with Nicola. Dr Goble, the very first psychiatrist who had seen her three years earlier, had talked about her 'anorexia nervosa'. His excitement building, Ed flicked through the 'A's in the index until he found the reference. Quickly turning the pages until he located the entry, he began reading it with intense interest. Unfortunately, it said little other than that anorexia nervosa was a complaint from which young women suffered who did not wish to grow up or face up to sexuality or leaving their parents.

Disappointed, he went back to the index to find further references under 'Endocrine Disorders'. One of these, headed 'Pathogenesis and Psychopathology' referred him back to the entry concerning anorexia nervosa. Half-heartedly he turned back to the page and then discovered that he'd made a mistake. The first time, he'd only read half the article. It continued on the next page. There he read about excessive eating and that sufferers induced themselves to vomit because they were afraid of becoming overweight. It went on to say that 'the loss of body fluid can lead to urinary infection, renal impairments and epileptic seizures'.

This final reference again excited him. Might Nicola's fainting fits have actually been epileptic seizures? He went back to the index and started reading the long list of entries under 'Epilepsy'. Some considerable time later, in a section on 'Epilepsy of the lower temporal lobe', he read that this was a cause of 'bizarre and unprovoked acts of violence'. He only just had time to note this down when the librarian announced that the library was closing.

It was late afternoon when Ed arrived home.

Pam was in the kitchen, preparing the evening meal and, greeting him with a tired smile, she asked, 'How did you get on at the library?'

Propping himself on a stool in the corner, Ed replied breezily, 'Tell me about Nicola first. How did you find her?'

Pam stopped washing the dishes and wiped her hands. Clearly saddened by her visit, she said, 'It was awful, Eddie. We were shown into a small room inside the medical unit. There was a table there, a chair on one side and two chairs on the other. Mo and I sat there waiting for Nicola and all of a sudden I heard this screaming: "I want my Mum. Where's my Mum? I want my Mum." I ran out and there was my Nicola being brought along the corridor with a wardress on each side. No shoes on her feet, a horrible thick canvas dress on. The sadness of it all – her hair looking awful, her face bloated, her eyes staring, unable to focus on anything . . .' Overcome by the horror of the remembrance she could never blot from her mind, Pam stopped. Before she could go on she had to wipe away the tears that had welled up in her eyes. 'When she saw me, she pulled away from the wardresses and ran to me. I just held her and then we walked into the room together. They weren't unkind to her, Eddie. I just sat there holding her hand, the other was wrapped in bandages because of the operation. I just wanted to bring Nicola home and cuddle her. My poor little girl. I feel so very sad for her all the time.'

Pam turned back to the sink and busied herself again with the dishes. Knowing that she needed a moment to compose herself, Ed waited a while before saying, 'I suppose that, as you were allowed to see Nicola, she hasn't attempted anything else since the incident in the bath?'

'I don't think they ever take their eyes off her, Eddie. I just can't stand the thought of her being kept in that cell, all alone . . .'

Getting off the stool, Ed walked across to his wife and put his arm comfortingly around her shoulder. Realizing, as the words came tumbling out, that they were inadequate consolation, he said, 'I know, I know, but at least it keeps her from killing herself.'

'I don't think she's our Nicola any more,' Pam sobbed. 'Our Nicola isn't there. She's gone away somewhere . . .'

Ed took a step backwards and, changing tack, said cheerily, 'Want some good news for a change?'

Pam managed to smile weakly. She knew she was going to hear about Ed's research whatever she said.

Ed was just about to launch into an account of his findings when Sally burst in through the kitchen door and asked excitedly, 'Did you find anything out, Dad?' She sat down on the stool Ed had vacated and waited expectantly.

With his audience assembled, Ed embarked on a blow-by-blow account of how his delving through the medical books in the library had led him to the discovery that sufferers of epilepsy in the lower temporal lobe committed unpremeditated acts of aggression and destructive violence. 'The effects of this type of epilepsy,' he concluded, 'are very similar to at least some of Nicola's behaviour.'

Sally was excited. 'That's funny,' she said. 'Who was it told me that when they visited Nicola she said she'd just had a brain scan and the doctor said she might have epilepsy?'

Ed was astonished. 'Why hasn't somebody told me?' he demanded.

'I don't know, Dad,' Sally replied. 'I've only just remembered it because of what you were saying. I can't even remember who told me what Nicola had said.'

Pam looked puzzled. 'I can't understand why they haven't informed us. It's a bit odd, don't you think?'

'They're not obliged to tell us anything,' Ed said. 'In any event, there may be nothing in it. How long ago was this, Sally?'

At first, Sally couldn't remember, but she worked out that it must have happened just before Nicola had slashed her hand. Pam then suggested that it might have been Barbara, a friend of Nicola's, who had visited her the day before.

The three of them rushed out of the kitchen and into the sitting-room where Pam picked up the phone. She was in such a hurry that she misdialled the number, had to replace the receiver and then redial.

'Hello, Mrs Jackson. It's Pam Owen. Is Barbara there?' Pam turned and nodded to Sally and Ed. 'Hello, Barbara . . . Yes, I saw her today . . . Well, we don't know for sure.' To the mounting frustration of the other two, Pam had then to give a brief description of Nicola's latest escapades. Finally, she was able to ask, 'Barb, you know that when you went in to see Nicola – about a couple of weeks ago, wasn't it? . . . Did Nicola mention anything to you about having a brain scan?' The tension mounted as Ed and Sally tried desperately to hear what was being said at the other end of the phone. 'Do you think Nicola was making that bit up? . . . Yes, epilepsy.' Ed was beside himself with impatience. 'We'll check with them on Monday. Thanks Barbara, you've been a great help.'

Pam quickly put the phone down and said, 'There's no doubt about it. Nicola told Barbara she had a brain scan and the doctor thought there were indications of epilepsy.' She paused for a moment and then added, 'Funnily enough, as soon as she said that I felt sure I'd heard of this epilepsy thing before, although I can't understand why.'

Trying desperately to trawl through distant memories, Pam sank down on to the settee. Sally sat on the arm of a chair and waited expectantly. Even though he felt as if he'd glimpsed the end of the rainbow, Ed tried to suppress any sense of jubilation and rushed back into the kitchen to collect his notes.

When he returned, Pam announced, 'I can't see it can be epilepsy!'

'Of course it can,' Ed replied dismissively. 'But we won't know for sure until I ring Holloway and speak to Dr Wells first thing on Monday morning.' Then, in capital letters, he added to his notes, NAT. ASSOC. EPILEPSY/ CHECK AND PHONE.'

'Do you think . . .' Sally said and then stopped as her parents looked at her. She started again, 'You saw Dr Morley on Thursday, didn't you?' They both nodded. 'Well, he said he'd discussed Nicola's case with Dr Wells, didn't he?' They nodded again. 'Well then, Dr Wells is the psychiatrist at Holloway and he would know about it, wouldn't he?' Both Ed and Pam kept their heads still and looked vaguely puzzled. 'What I mean is that the brain scan was over two weeks ago and they'd have the results by now and if they'd found Nicola had epilepsy then Dr Morley would know about it and he would have mentioned it to you even if he knew that you hadn't been told by Dr Wells.'

Ed and Pam were taken aback and just a little amused at their daughter's perceptive outburst.

'Maybe he did, Sally,' Ed said thoughtfully.

'What do you mean?' Pam enquired.

'Well, Dr Morley did mention a second illness and maybe that's what he was hinting at.'

Pam couldn't accept that this was possible. 'Why should he hint at it, Ed? Why wouldn't he have come right out and told us?'

The obvious reason struck Ed as his wife was asking the question. 'Because I've been assuming, or at least hoping, that epilepsy of the lower temporal lobe could be cured and so Nicola could return home. But if it's not, in their jargon, "susceptible to treatment", then she would still have to be sent to Broadmoor.'

Long before Ed had stopped answering her question, Pam had stopped listening. A picture was forming in her mind. 'I think I've remembered where it was that I'd heard about Nicola having a brain scan,' she said hesitantly. 'I think . . .'

She jumped up and rushed from the room into the office. Within seconds she returned, holding a letter. 'Here it is,' she said. 'I know this is terrible but it's a letter from Nicola. It came while you were away and I just put it in the filing tray and forgot about it.'

'Well, what does it say about epilepsy?' Sally asked, desperate to prevent a family row erupting.

Ed was about to take the letter because he wanted to read it all, but Sally's timely interruption allowed Pam to carry on. 'It's this bit,' she said and then read from towards the end of the letter: 'I saw Dr Wells today and he enquired after my health. After speaking to me for some time, he said I was quite seriously depressed, although he is still going to continue with the same treatment. He has also had the results of my EEG tests which have proved positive. He explained to me that this meant that I had a mild form of epilepsy or something similar . . .' She stopped reading and, handing the letter to her husband, said, 'I'm ever so sorry I mislaid it, Ed.'

He was so excited by this new information that it was impossible for him to be angry. 'Don't worry, love,' he said. 'You've more than enough on your plate at the moment.'

As he read Nicola's letter on the lined notepaper stamped 'Holloway Prison', he became even more determined that he would not only ensure his daughter's release from prison but that he'd move heaven and earth to find somebody who would be able to cure her. It was something that, throughout the previous five years, the medical profession had signally failed to do.

Ed had planned to spend Monday working in the office at home on a client's report, but the first thing he did was to track down and telephone the National Association of Epilepsy. He spoke to an efficient-sounding woman whose tone softened markedly when he announced that he thought his daughter was suffering from epilepsy of the lower temporal lobe. She promised to send some literature about epilepsy immediately. (Unfortunately, when the booklets arrived, none of them made any mention of the lower temporal lobe.)

He had less success in trying to contact Dr Wells at Holloway. After his third failure, he asked if the doctor would ring back as soon as he was free. An hour later, Dr Wells called. After thanking him for phoning, Ed asked him if Nicola was suffering from a form of epilepsy.

'Definitely not,' Dr Wells replied.

'But, according to Nicola, her Electroencephalogram had shown up abnormalities.'

'Slight abnormalities. But they were not so abnormal, given her medication and the stressful situation of her confinement.'

Ed was not satisfied. 'I've been reading up on epilepsy,' he said, 'and what forcibly struck me was the description of the behaviour of victims suffering epilepsy of the lower temporal lobe. There were marked similarities with Nicola's bizarre behaviour. One gains the distinct impression that it is incurable and in some cases the sufferers have to be confined in a secure establishment. Is that the case with Nicola? My wife and I would rather know the truth, Dr Wells.'

'Believe me, Mr Owen, the medical staff at Holloway are extremely thorough and I can again assure you that Nicola is not suffering from any form of epilepsy.'

Ed thanked the doctor for being so open and put down the phone. As he leant back in his swivel chair, he did not know whether to be relieved or disappointed. He was, however, determined that the quest would go on. He pulled open the left-hand drawer of the desk, took out the notes he'd made at the library, and carefully reread them.

He took a fresh sheet of paper and wrote:

NO EPILEPSY
1. DOES ENDOCRINE DISORDER = HORMONE DISORDER?

2. OVARIES ARE PART OF THE ENDOCRINE SYSTEM. FIND OUT WHAT HORMONES, IF ANY, THEY SECRETE.
3. IF ENDOCRINE DISORDER = HORMONE DISORDER, THEN WHAT HAPPENS TO MENSTRUATION?

### NICOLA'S PERIODS

Satisfied, Ed put down his pen and opened his diary. The entries confirmed what he already knew. His schedule that week was so busy that there was no possibility of his finding the time to go again to the library until Saturday. He could but hope that, despite his total lack of medical training, he'd be able to find out the cause of Nicola's problems before it was too late. It couldn't be long before her case came to court and then, unless a miracle happened, the doctors' recommendation would be accepted – 'Disposal Broadmoor'.

When Ed told Pam what Dr Wells had said, the news that their new-found hopes appeared to have been dashed did not seem to upset her. But, later that evening, when she and Ed were alone in the sitting-room, Pam, without warning, started an agonized wail that increased in volume, as she rocked backwards and forwards on the settee with her arms crossed tightly across her body and her fingers clawing at her sides, until it became a piteous scream of, 'No! No! No! Please no!'

Ed rushed across to her, dropping on his knees to peer closely at her face. 'What is it? Tell me what it is, Pamsie,' he urged, deeply concerned.

No longer able to endure the torment, she gasped, 'I don't want her to go there . . . I . . . I just can't . . . I can't live with the thought of her being locked away in that place.'

Ed didn't respond and for a while she just wept. He did his best to comfort her, holding her rigid hands in his and looking into her fear-shot eyes.

Then she let out a heart-rending cry and screamed, 'I wish she were dead! I wish she were dead!' Her scream faded and her last words were a barely audible mumble. 'She'll only die inch by inch in that place.' Her head dropped down into her lap and her whole body shook with violent convulsions.

Ed firmly took hold of her head and lifted it up. He stared directly into her unseeing eyes and with a note of steel said, 'Dead? Dead? You want our daughter dead? I can't fight the grave. There's no coming back from death. Death's permanent. Do you understand? Permanent. There's no second chance. No chance at all. It's the bloody end!' He studied her face and saw that her terror had subsided. He gently kissed her forehead and reassuringly said, 'We can beat this thing together, Pamsie. Don't you understand? Don't, please don't lose faith in what we know and believe. Those people out there will have to listen to us. We'll make them listen, I promise you. But I need your strength. I can't do it without you.' He stopped holding her and sat back on his heels.

Pam's body began to relax and the trembling stopped. Slowly, tentatively, her hand reached out and lovingly brushed Ed's cheek.

# CHAPTER SEVENTEEN

## *Progress*

Every day that week, Pam made sure that somebody visited Nicola. If she didn't go herself, she'd phone the medical unit to enquire about Nicola. The officers there were always courteous and informative. As Jean Harrison, the medical supervisor, had promised, Nicola's behaviour and mood swings were recorded and the unit staff enthusiastically reported to Pam the remarkable improvements that were made during the week. There were no more hysterical scenes or aggressive outbursts. Officers noted that Nicola instinctively stood up when they entered her cell. She greeted them with 'Good-morning' or 'Good-evening' and smilingly said 'Thank you' when her meals were delivered.

The nature of the strip-cell regime was such that any noticeable improvement in behaviour was rewarded. On Tuesday, Nicola was provided with a pillow and so sleeping on the bare mattress was slightly more comfortable. On Wednesday, the strip dress was exchanged for a simple cotton smock. On Thursday, she was given laceless slip-on canvas shoes. On Friday, a chair was brought into the cell so that, for the first time in over a fortnight, she could sit down to eat her meals instead of having to squat on the floor.

On Friday too, Ed and Pam visited Nicola. They kissed and held her hand and assured her that she would soon be coming home to them. At the end of the visit, the two wardresses looked away as, contrary to prison regulations,

Ed and Pam held their sobbing daughter for a brief moment before she was led away. They stood in the corridor and watched Nicola's every step as she was escorted back to her cell. At the door, she turned and Ed confidently shouted to her, 'We shall win, Nicola. We shall win – make no mistake about it. You'll be home soon. We promise.'

He did not know how they were going to keep that promise; he only knew that they would.

Later that day, Jonathan telephoned. 'Hello, Dad,' he said, 'I've been picked for a house match tomorrow. Kick off is ten-thirty. Can you make it?'

Ed laughed and asked, 'What sort of notice is that, Johnnie?'

'Sorry, Dad, I was reserve and didn't expect to play but one of the team's gone down with a bad cold or something.'

'So what position are you playing, Johnnie?'

'Full back, of course.'

Ed smiled. It had been his position when, long before Johnnie had been born, long before even Nicola was born, he'd played for a season in a semi-professional football league. 'Of course I'll come,' he said cheerily, although for a fleeting second it had crossed his mind to say that he wouldn't be able to make it. He'd just received a letter from Mr Smythe, his solicitor, advising him that it was possible that the case against Nicola might be put on the Warned List at the Old Bailey for the following week. He only had Saturday to tackle the further research he needed to do in the public library. But how could he reject his son's request? He was all too aware that, for so many months, Johnnie and Sally had taken second place to Nicola, not in his and Pam's affections but in the time and attention they'd been given.

'That's great!' Johnnie exclaimed, genuinely pleased. 'Must go now, Dad. We're not allowed to hog the phone. See you at ten-thirty tomorrow. And don't be late!'

Ed was on time for the match and thoroughly enjoyed watching Johnnie and his school friends enthusiastically playing the game he'd loved so much as a young man. He noted that there were two or three promising players but their skill was more often than not negated by the brute force and flying boots of the others. Like peas being rolled around the inside of a biscuit tin, all the red-faced youngsters charged in a mass wherever the ball went. Only one goal was scored – by the other side. But Ed was delighted that Johnnie had acquitted himself so well. Clearly, the other members of his team felt so too. On three separate occasions, they showed their appreciation, with much backslapping, of the surgical precision with which he brought down a burly opponent.

After the match, Ed chatted both to Johnnie and his housemaster. That took more time and so it was a little after midday before he was able to climb into his car and set off through the heavy Saturday traffic to the library at Bexleyheath.

As soon as he arrived, Ed headed straight for the medical section. First, he took out the volumes he'd used the previous Saturday and then he selected some further titles that he thought might contain some relevant information. It was fortunate that the library was almost empty, because Ed needed the table-space of two readers to accommodate his vast pile of weighty books.

From his inside pocket, he took the notes he had previously made and carefully straightened them out on the table. This time, he'd brought only one pen. That too was placed strategically in front of him.

Working through the indexes of the books, he carefully noted any subheadings of key words that needed fuller definitions or investigation. An hour and a half later, he leaned back in his chair and stared out of the window. He'd clarified nothing, found no new leads and was feeling increasingly frustrated.

Afraid that once again he might have come to a dead end, Ed turned to another of his reference books to look up progesterone in the index. As he was doing so, he suddenly saw the word 'Premenstrual'. Two entries later were the words 'Premenstrual Tension'. He turned quickly to the page that was given and, as he read through the article, he made further notes with a growing sense of excitement: 'A syndrome occurring in the days prior to menstruation. Symptoms = headaches, insomnia, fatigue, emotional instablility.'

He sat for a few minutes thinking about what he should do or read next. Deciding that he needed help, he walked across to the tall, bespectacled, dark-haired woman who was the only librarian on duty.

'I wonder if you can help me,' he enquired with a politeness that only barely masked his sense of urgency. 'I'm trying to read up on premenstrual syndrome. I'm not so much interested in the causes. I think I've managed to find out enough about them. What I'm more interested in is . . .' For a moment, he couldn't think how best to express what it was he wanted. 'What I'm more interested in is the behaviour of young women suffering from it and there doesn't seem to be much on that particular aspect in the reference books.'

The librarian turned to her right and looked down at the bottom shelf of what appeared to be a special bookcase. 'I've something here that might help,' she said, producing a chunky book with a shiny paper wrapper of light green banded with white. She turned to the index, quickly flicked through the pages and began to read.

Ed watched with a confused mixture of excitement, hope, fear and panic.

She shook her head slowly and said decisively, 'No, this isn't it.'

A sharp, sickening pang of disappointment.

She quickly turned back to the index and said, 'I think this may be it.' Then finding another place in the book, she again started reading. After a few seconds, she triumphantly turned the book round, set it down on the counter and with a carefully manicured index finger pointed to where he should begin reading. Ed looked down at the page, but the librarian said, with a smile, 'You can take it over to where you're working. It's all right.'

Ed quickly returned to the table and studied the selected text which described the behaviour typical of women suffering from the emotional stress of premenstrual syndrome. It referred to 'repeated acts of violence of a criminal nature . . . hysteria . . .'

He'd almost come to the end of the disappointingly short passage, when he became aware of the librarian standing behind him. He looked up, as she said, 'This is an American book that's just arrived. It deals with the subject more comprehensively.'

Moving the book he'd been reading to one side to accommodate the one she handed to him, he said gratefully, 'Thank you. That's very kind of you.'

It was a thick volume, open at a chapter headed 'Premenstrual Syndrome'. Its pages were each divided into three columns of small but clear print.

The opening section dealt with the possible causes that were already familiar to him but, as he read on, it was as though a bright light had suddenly been shed on what had been until then a darkened world of doubt and fear. Describing the results of researches carried out on college campuses, the chapter gave vivid descriptions of sufferers' behaviour.

'I'm sorry. We're closing now,' the librarian announced. So engrossed had Ed been in his reading that he hadn't been aware that she was standing beside his table. 'I'm sorry to interrupt you, but it's already past the closing time.'

He looked straight at her. 'You can't close,' he said, desperate and defiant. 'This is a matter of life or death. I've almost finished!' He glanced back at the chapter to assess how much more time he needed. 'You must allow me ten more minutes,' he pleaded, the tension etched across his face. 'I'm not exaggerating. This matter is urgent. A young woman's life may depend upon what I learn here!'

'All right,' she said, 'but only ten more minutes.'

As she turned to walk away, Ed softly said to her, 'It's my daughter, you see. They want to send her to Broadmoor.' Then he returned to his reading.

He was just finishing the chapter when the librarian returned. 'I'm sorry. I really must close now.'

Ed glanced down at his watch. That Saturday, Bexleyheath Public Library would be closing thirty-five minutes late. 'I'm so sorry,' he said. 'You've been so kind and helpful. Let me help you put the books back.'

With a weary smile, she declined his offer.

Back in his car, Ed made no attempt to start the engine. Sitting with his hands loosely holding the steering-wheel, he pondered on what he had learned and what he should do next. He found it astonishing that in a small suburban library he had read an American medical book that accurately and comprehensively described his daughter's behaviour – self-mutilation, destruction of personal possessions, physical assaults on loved ones, suicide attempts, excessive eating and self-induced vomiting. Yet this was a catalogue of bizarre acts performed by a number of separate sufferers. Nicola had managed to perform them all and, in addition, had committed not one act of arson but two.

But there were many questions still left unanswered. If so much was apparently known about premenstrual syndrome, why had no reference been made to it by any of the doctors who had attended Nicola at various times over the last four years? Although Dr Morley's mention of the endocrine had started the whole voyage of discovery, wouldn't he have been more specific if he was really aware of premenstrual syndrome? Dr Sangster may well have suspected something when he wanted Nicola to be seen by a gynaecologist, but why did nothing come of that? And why, when there was so much evidence that there was something physically wrong with Nicola had she always been treated as though she had only mental problems and so was given regular and massive doses of tranquillizers?

It was only at this point that a sudden realization struck him as forcefully as if he'd been unexpectedly kicked by a mule. He gasped out aloud, 'There wasn't a single bloody mention of anything that could be done about the condition – not a single bloody thing! There was no prognosis, no bloody cure for premenstrual syndrome!'

As he started the car, there was only one thought in his mind: oh, dear God, please don't let it be another temporal lobe case! The fear grew that, after all, the doctors had correctly diagnosed Nicola's illness but that they'd had an obvious reason for remaining silent – the condition was incurable. The thought all but made him sick.

By the time he arrived home, all his earlier euphoria and certainties had evaporated. As he opened the front door, he did his best to compose himself so that his disappointment and fear were not written large on his face.

Pam was in the kitchen, peeling potatoes for the evening meal. 'How did you get on?' she asked perfunctorily, not even bothering to look up.

He carefully considered his reply before saying, 'The librarian was very helpful and found an American medical book for me. It's quite amazing really. I've been reading all about Nicola or rather about all the odd and terrible things she's been doing.' He waited for a response, but none came. Pam continued busying herself with the potatoes. 'You know Dr Morley referred to the endocrine?' he asked, trying to prompt some response. None came. 'Well, it looks as if a disorder in the endocrine system can mess up the supply of hormones from the ovaries.'

'Really. That's very interesting,' Pam said, without the slightest hint of interest or conviction, the thought of another disappointment making her cautious.

Ed battled on. 'One of the hormones, an important one for the well being of the female, is called something like progesteron, or something like that – I forget its proper name. Anyway, if the female body doesn't receive a proper supply of this hormone, the woman suffers badly for several days immediately before and after the start of her periods.'

'That happens to a lot of women. What's new about that?'

'What this American book talks about isn't just having a few off-days but severe cases where women go berserk, so berserk that they'll destroy anything including themselves. It stops just short of saying that women who suffer from premenstrual syndrome can go crazy for a time.'

Pam was still unmoved, but she did her best to humour him. 'Why don't you write it up for Mr Smythe? I'm sure he'll be interested.' She turned to him and smiled. 'Go on, Eddie. I'll type it first thing Monday morning and he'll have it by Tuesday.'

'All right, but I want to think about it some more before I put pen to paper. I'm going to take Emma for a walk.'

As he went to collect the dog's lead, Pam said, 'And what about Johnnie? You haven't told me how he was this morning.'

Ed immediately felt guilty. Despite his best intentions, the crusade to save Nicola had totally preoccupied him. How could he have forgotten to tell Pam about his visit to Johnnie's school? But he had. Speaking in a much more relaxed way, he gave his wife an amusing but accurate summary of what Johnnie had done, adding that his housemaster reported that their son was doing well and appeared to be happy at school. Then he called Emma in from the garden.

While Ed walked twice round the outer limits of the woods, Emma, with all her boundless energy, rushed off in all directions chasing squirrels and then returning to check that Ed was still there. Sometimes she'd burst out of the bushes a few yards ahead and at other times she'd run up from behind, brushing her body against his legs as though to announce, 'I'm here!'

As they walked back towards Camden Road, Emma was panting and her saliva-drenched tongue lolled out of her open mouth.

'Hello, Mr Owen.'

Ed had been so preoccupied that he hadn't even seen the young woman approaching, but as soon as she spoke he recognized that it was Geraldine, a person who'd worked in the cost office of a firm where he'd been the financial controller.

'Oh, hello, Jo,' he said enthusiastically. As he'd always called her by the wrong name, she didn't bother to correct him.

They hadn't seen each other for some years and Geraldine explained that she'd recently married and that she and her husband had just bought a house near by. After sharing anecdotal memories of mutual friends, Geraldine asked pleasantly, 'And how is Nicola? The last time I saw her was in the pantomime at Swanley playing the Principal Boy. Now when was that? I suppose it must have been two years ago. She was so good. I expect she's gone on to great things now, hasn't she?'

Ed studied her face. It was obvious that she knew nothing of recent events and so he said, 'You can't have heard about Nicola.' Then he explained about the fire and what had happened subsequently to his daughter. After saying that the doctors had been unable to find a cure for her, he told her something of the work he'd been doing in the library, concluding, 'I think it's got something to do with a thing called premenstrual syndrome which is all to do with hormones being upset by some disorder of what is—'

Geraldine interrupted him excitedly. 'There was a huge article in one of the women's magazines on exactly that subject. I think I've still got it. If I have, I'll drop

it round to you. You could try and contact the author. I
think her name's Dr Dalton.'

'Dr Dalton? What does she do?'

'She runs a special clinic where she treats women who
have severe problems with their periods. She knows all
about it and she's developed a treatment that sorts it
all out.'

Having heard this news, Ed returned home in great
excitement. Less than an hour later, two pages pulled from
a magazine were pushed through the letter-box. The title
of the article was 'Are Your Periods Driving You Mad?'

Pam and Ed read it together and for the first time
felt real hope. The illness Dr Dalton described could
apparently be treated. There was a cure.

That night, as they lay together, quietly reflecting on
what the future might now hold, Pam gently placed a
hand on his naked chest and with complete conviction
declared, 'We're going to win, Ed Owen!'

\*　　\*　　\*

On Sunday, I awoke early because my hand was very
painful and felt about as dainty as I would have looked
in a tutu. I was still lying down on my mattress when
the two officers entered, locking the door behind them.
I pretended to be asleep because it seemed surprisingly
early for them to come in and I was curious to see what
they were going to do. To my delight, one of them stood
on my chair and opened the shutters of my window so
that the soft light of a mellow autumn morning flooded
into the room.

'How lovely,' I sighed.

'What was that, Nicola?' one of the officers asked.

'I said it's lovely,' I croaked emotionally. Then,
finding my voice, I added, 'Thank you.' But it was such
an extraordinary experience, having daylight in my cell at
last, that I began to cry.

'Well, if it upsets you, love,' the wardress teased, 'I'll close the shutters for you!'

'No, thank you,' I said, perking up. 'There's no need to go to any trouble for me.' That even raised a smile. Sitting up on my mattress, I looked towards the light. 'It looks as though it's a beautiful morning.'

'It is,' she agreed, 'and breakfast will be served in a few minutes.'

The officers unlocked the door and were about to leave when one turned and said, 'Nicola, would you like a bath later?'

'I'd love one,' I replied. 'Thank you.'

After they'd gone, I looked around my cell for the first time in daylight. There wasn't much to see, but then I noticed something completely unexpected. On the chair was a plastic mug filled with fresh freesias. The officer must have put them there when she opened the shutters.

It was a perfect start to what promised to be a better day.

\*     \*     \*

Later that Sunday morning, a rare event took place in the Owen household. Not only had Pam awoken before Ed, she'd crept downstairs and laid a breakfast tray with tea and an assortment of biscuits. With Emma at her heels, she entered the bedroom and, imitating Ed's typical reveille, woke him with the breezy words, 'Good morning, Edward. It's a beautiful morning with a full sun coming up over Bexley Woods. The still air is full of autumnal fragrance!'

He was smiling before his eyes opened.

Sensing that there was something special about the occasion, Emma broke the house rules and jumped on to the bed. As she began to lick Ed's face, he protested, 'I'll wash later if you don't mind, Emma!'

Peering through the window at the russet hues of the woods beyond, Pam said, 'Why don't we drink our tea on the balcony?'

'A splendid idea,' Ed replied and climbed out of bed. He put on his slippers and sat down next to Pam on the balcony.

Emma joined them and eagerly peered out in case an intrepid squirrel happened to be passing. As there didn't seem to be any, the dog looked round at Ed and Pam to check whether they'd reached the same conclusion and then, seeing that they obviously weren't even looking, settled down at Pam's feet.

'We're going to have a battle on our hands,' Pam said.

'Don't I know it.'

'I'm sure the lawyer thinks the only defence is insanity. He's got to be convinced that Nicola can be treated.'

'I know that, Pam. The problem is that she has acted as though she were mad. We've still got to find out for sure what is wrong with her and then whether she can be cured. That's the important thing. That's what's necessary to stop her being sent to Broadmoor.'

'Well, the article says that the premenstrual thing can be cured and Dr Dalton knows how it can be done.'

'But we've got so little time. At least Smythe has told us that Nicola's case definitely won't be heard next week, but it could happen any time after that. First thing tomorrow, I'm going to ring him and tell him what we've discovered.'

Sharing his enthusiastic determination, Pam added, 'And we'll send him a photocopy of the article.'

'Good thinking, Pamsie. We'll also send one to Dr Wells and Dr Morley. It might be an education for them! And I'll write a quick note to Nicola. If I post it at the central sorting office, she should get it tomorrow.'

'Don't start telling her too much and building castles in the sky for her, Eddie.'

'I won't do that, I just want to tell her again that we love her and are doing everything we can for her.' Putting an arm fondly round his wife, he added with a smile, 'We don't have such a difficult task! It's only all the others we've got to convince that we're right!'

216

# CHAPTER EIGHTEEN

## *In Some Disarray*

On Sunday evening, for the first time in the three weeks I had spent in the strip cell, I was allowed to wear a night-dress.

All the officers who visited me said how delighted they were with the obvious improvement in my behaviour. 'You're now a totally different Nicola,' one of them told me.

And, little by little, I began to feel that I was becoming a different person. At first, I thought this was because Dr Wells had decided to take me off tranquillizers because, he said, they were the reason why I was finding it difficult to sleep. Then I began to wonder if the lifting of my black depression was due to the new pill Dr Wells had prescribed. I didn't know what it was, but he said it was a form of hormone pill that would regulate my menstrual cycle and could well have other beneficial results.

The better I began to feel, the more I began to worry that the change might be temporary. In the past, there always seemed to have been some days, even weeks, when the old Nicola returned and I could deal with all the things going on around me. But such times never lasted for long. So I was constantly afraid of what tomorrow might bring. For all I knew, I might wake up in the morning with nothing in my mind but the determination to end it all.

On Monday morning, I was taken to the medical supervisor's office to be interviewed by Dr Wells. 'How are you feeling, Nicola?' he asked as soon as I'd sat down.

'Much better, thank you. I think this new medication is really helping me,' I replied honestly.

Dr Wells seemed to ignore my reply. He was reading the day reports he'd taken from the bulky file on his desk. Without looking up, he said to the medical supervisor, 'I take it that nothing has been left out?'

Sounding a little annoyed, she replied, 'Since the bathroom incident, there has been nothing further. Her behaviour has been consistent and stable. We have been able to follow the procedure and reward her good conduct.' She then quickly ran through the list of rewards I'd been given during the previous week.

Dr Wells looked up at me. For the moment, he was silent. Then he said, 'I have made application to the Central Office of the Department of Health for a residency for you at Broadmoor.' He paused, but I said nothing. 'They have the facilities there,' he continued, 'to provide the proper treatment and I'm sure that, in time, you will benefit from their care and experience.'

Not knowing what else to say, I replied, 'Thank you, Dr Wells.'

He then stood up, picked up his papers and left the small room.

The medical supervisor smiled at me and said, 'Broadmoor is an excellent hospital. It's situated in magnificent gardens among the Surrey hills. I've been there several times and I don't think you'll be unhappy there.'

I said nothing. There was nothing to say. My only concern was that moving anywhere might delay my return home. Christmas wasn't very far away and I wanted desperately to spend it with Mum and Dad.

*　　*　　*

218

Well aware that the time was running out for him to halt the slow but monstrous wheels of a bureaucracy that had decided to despatch Nicola to Broadmoor, Ed phoned Mr Smythe that Monday morning.

'We've got hold of this article called "Are Your Periods Driving You Mad?", he said enthusiastically. 'I'm going to send you a copy of it today. It vividly describes bizarre acts committed by sufferers of what is called premenstrual syndrome. I read of the same sort of thing in a medical reference book in the library. It was an American book as a matter of fact. What's so interesting is that this is a medical illness that doesn't appear to be widely recognized or fully understood by the medical profession. But the important point is that it is a medical illness and it is susceptible to treatment. There's a Dr Katharina Dalton who apparently knows all about this problem and can treat it successfully by all accounts.'

'Dalton. How do you spell that?'

'D – a – l – t – o – n.'

'And what's the address of her clinic?'

'The article just says she works at University College Hospital.'

'Right, Mr Owen, I'll try and make contact with her there.'

'Thank you, Mr Smythe. You've no need for me to tell you . . .' Ed's voice petered out – concern replacing his initial enthusiasm.

'I'm sure it's most useful information,' the solicitor replied. 'I'll read the article with interest. Now, if we've finished with that issue, I'd like to move on to something else. In fact, I was just about to give you a ring when you called. I've just received a copy of Dr Boardman's report.'

'Is his hospital willing to take Nicola?' Ed asked anxiously.

'Apparently not.'

'Why? What reason did he give?'

'It's quite a long report and I'm sending it on to you.'

'But the main points? Can you just let me know what they are?'

'If you wish, Mr Owen. I have to say that, as I see it, the report doesn't really carry the matter any further. Dr Boardman refers to Nicola having been a rather timid child who was for a considerable period excessively frightened of animals—'

'That's rubbish,' Ed interrupted. 'What does he mean "excessively"? She cried when a dog was first brought into the house. After that, she's always loved animals.'

'Shall I go on, Mr Owen?' the solicitor said coldly.

'Please do. I won't interrupt again.'

'Then Dr Boardman talks about her early adolescence and the development of her problems. I'll read his final paragraph: "In conclusion, then, Nicola shows evidence of serious emotional and personality development, and at present could be described as a hysterical psychopath. Although suffering, in my view, from a psychopathic disorder within the meaning of the 1959 Mental Health Act, the likelihood of this disorder being susceptible to treatment is highly debatable. Certainly, if it can be done at all, it can only be carried out in a specific type of setting which is not easily obtainable." '

'That means Broadmoor,' Ed snapped angrily.

'If they will agree to take her.'

That was too much. Ed exploded. 'I know what all this is about,' he shouted. 'All these doctors are in collusion.'

'What on earth do you mean by that?' Mr Smythe snapped back.

Immediately, Ed regretted losing his temper. 'Perhaps that is a bit strong, Mr Smythe. But what I mean is that they appear to back each other up so that they're all saying the same thing. The impression I get is that each new doctor that comes on the scene looks at the previous doctor's report and goes on from there. Collusion is the wrong word. Sorry about that. To be honest, I believe that the medical profession has let Nicola down. The doctors all want to say that she's been emotionally ill from childhood. It's all balls and we'll have none of it.'

Ignoring what he considered to be Ed's unnecessarily crude expression, Mr Smythe replied, 'Although the case against Nicola hasn't yet come up in the Warned List, it will do so shortly and that means she can then be called for trial at any time.'

'We'll have to delay it,' Ed said determinedly. 'We need more time – more time to find out about the medical aspects the trick cyclists have ignored. There's not a shadow of a doubt in my mind, nor in Mrs Owen's, that the root cause of Nicola's problems is medical and not psychiatric. We've constantly referred to links between Nicola's menstrual cycle and her problems, but we've largely been ignored. So we're counting on you to do what you can, Mr Smythe.'

Mr Smythe was used to dealing with difficult people and rarely lost his temper, but there was much about Ed Owen's manner and behaviour that he didn't like. In particular, he resented the man's stubborn insistence that the experts who were doing their best to help his daughter were wrong or incompetent. 'I'll do what I can,' he said brusquely, intending to bring the conversation to a close. 'I shall have a word with Mr Giacomo, your counsel, and then let you know where we are. I shall almost certainly write to you within the week.' He paused and added, 'I trust that you do not doubt our determination to do our best for Nicola. I take my responsibilities for my client very seriously, Mr Owen, very seriously indeed.'

'I have never doubted your commitment, Mr Smythe, and I'm very grateful for it. But, you must understand that, although Nicola is your client, she also happens to be our daughter and we love her. My God, we really do!'

Ed's telephone conversation with Mr Smythe increased his fear that the lawyers, like the so-called expert psychiatrists, had made up their minds that a residency in Broadmoor would be in Nicola's best interests. To achieve this, they would remove her from the penal system by entering a plea of insanity.

The arrival of Dr Boardman's report the following morning only served to increase his fears and bitter frustration. 'Look at this, Pam,' he screamed with rage, jabbing an index finger at the offending paragraph. 'He says, "She seems to have had very little sexual experience and says that the thought of it disgusts and revolts her. She has had no steady boyfriends at any time." That's a lie. What about Mark? What about Peter? I don't know where he gets all this from, but he's not describing the Nicola we know.'

'It seems they don't believe us when we say she was a normal, healthy young girl,' Pam said. Always able not only to calm her husband down but to come up with a sensible, practical proposal, she continued, 'What we must do is get a dozen or so people who've known Nicola really well to write directly to the solicitor. And her school reports. Why didn't I think of it before? I'll send those to Mr Smythe as well.'

'Good thinking, Pamsie,' Ed responded.

Pam immediately set to work on her plan, phoning friends and relatives and then searching for Nicola's school reports among the papers that had survived the fire.

For Ed, a period of intense activity had come to an end. Having discovered what he felt sure was the primary cause of Nicola's problems, he'd handed the information over to the experts and was forced to sit back and wait. Suiting neither his mood nor his temperament, this only added to his intense frustration and sense of gloom. He slept badly, only pecked at his food and considerably increased his consumption of whisky. At any moment, the raging bull locked up inside him was likely to break out and charge.

The letter he received a few days later from Mr Smythe did nothing to pacify him. 'Look at this, Pam,' he fumed. 'Giacomo is talking about another two doctors being required to identify the treatment necessary. The bloody sod doesn't listen! He and Smythe just aren't listening! They're all the bloody same – backing each other up on the safe option. Not one of them will stick an inch of his bloody neck above the parapet. They're covering their own backsides, protecting their own professional position. I'm sick of the whole bloody lot!' With that, he threw the letter on the floor.

'Ed, calm down for heaven's sake,' Pam declared. 'Your attitude is not helping.'

'You'll see what I mean when you've read the letter, Pam. They've already made up their minds.'

'Mr Smythe is an excellent solicitor, Ed. He is really trying to help Nicola.'

'I know, I know, but the fact remains he's part of the bloody system!' He was now shouting. 'Disposal, Nicola's disposal. That's what the system wants. It processes people like legs of lamb in a bloody meat packing plant. Bloody disposal!'

'You're not helping Nicola by being like this, Ed. If you turn them against you, then any hope we have of winning them over to our view will be lost. If that happens, we lose Nicola. Just think about that before you do any more bellowing.'

Ed sank back in the chair. 'You're right,' he said quietly. 'I know you're right. I'm not thinking straight.' After a moment, his composure regained, he announced, 'We must arrange to see both Mr Giacomo and Dr Wells. And another thing. I must write to Mr Smythe. We must get our views on record.'

Pam thought about this before saying, 'I think you should wait until after you've seen Nicola on Saturday before writing to Mr Smythe. Then you can give him up-to-date information. She seems to be getting better every day.'

Ed nodded in agreement.

'Oh, this will cheer you up,' Pam said brightly. 'Jonathan phoned to say he's coming home this weekend and he'd like to go with you to see Nicola.'

Two days later, as Ed drove Johnnie back home after their visit to Nicola, they sat for some miles in thoughtful silence.

'I think she's looking very well, Dad,' Johnnie said at last. 'It must cheer you up to see her looking so good and talking so sensibly.'

'It does, Johnnie. It really does. We're getting reports back every day from the friends who visit her and every day the reports are good and getting better.'

'And what's this new treatment she's on, the white pill she said she has to take every day? Perhaps that's helping.'

'I don't really know what it is. I spoke to the prison doctor on the phone yesterday but he didn't tell me much about it.'

'Didn't he say anything?'

'Just that it's a sort of birth-control pill.'

'A birth-control pill! In prison! What's that for?'

'I don't know. As far as I can gather, birth-control pills contain a mixture of hormones, so perhaps it's a way of giving Nicola some sort of hormone treatment.'

Although Johnnie felt somewhat out of his depth, the word 'hormones' did ring a bell for him. 'Isn't that what you and Mum said was wrong with Nicola – her hormones?'

'More or less. I've been talking a lot about it to Mr Smythe, the solicitor.'

'And what does he say about it? He sounds a good bloke to me.'

'Yes,' Ed laughed. 'He's a good bloke who thinks I'm a bit crazy!'

Relieved that the mood had lightened, Johnnie felt safe to reply, 'Well let's be fair, Dad, everybody thinks you're a bit crazy!'

At this, they both laughed. Despite – or perhaps because of – having to live through the nightmare of the previous months, the family had come closer together than ever before.

Although Johnnie knew his parents were working so hard for Nicola, he felt they were making the weekends when he came home special for him. For the first time, he realized he really loved his parents and knew they loved him. He could see that his sisters' dancing and music successes were no longer important. His parents' concern now was for their family. It was about people and not merely their achievements.

On Sunday evening, after taking Johnnie back to his boarding-school, Ed sat down to compose his letter to Mr Smythe. Several hours later, he completed his detailed statement of why he and his wife believed that 'the psychiatrists' reports dealt only with the symptoms of the illness and not the illness or illnesses that create the symptoms they have observed and commented upon.' Having given a mass of information to support his contention that 'at least part of Nicola's emotional problem is directly connected with the menstruation cycle,' Ed's letter concluded, 'We believe that a serious mistake was made with Nicola's situation way back, four years ago. We cannot undo that but we feel strongly that a decision of such importance must only be reached after exhaustive examinations and research for medical facts.'

The following morning, after he'd posted his letter to Mr Smythe, Ed again phoned Dr Wells at the medical centre in Holloway. There was something vital he needed to know.

'I hope you don't mind my asking,' he said, 'but what is this new treatment – the birth-control pill?'

'In Nicola's case, of course, I'm not concerned with birth control,' Dr Wells replied, 'but with regulating her menstrual cycle. Like all oral contraceptives, Duphaston, which is the name of the pill Nicola is being given, has as its basis something called progestogens.'

'Is that the same as progesterone?' Ed asked.

Surprised by the question, Dr Wells replied, 'Indeed, Mr Owen, they are very similar. Progestogens are a synthetic version of progesterone. Nicola is being given the pill for a specified number of days, commencing on the twelfth day of her menstrual cycle.'

'Am I correct in thinking that was the day after my wife and I had visited Miss Harrison, the medical supervisor? She said something about your starting a new treatment the following day.'

'I believe it was, Mr Owen.'

'Thank you, Dr Wells, that's very interesting. As I'm sure you know, the pill seems to have had an amazing effect. I saw Nicola on Saturday and she seemed so much better. What do you think?'

'There has certainly been a remarkable change in her, particularly with the onset of her menstruation.'

For the first time in his life, Ed felt his heart leap. He resisted the temptation to say, 'We told you so,' and instead asked, 'Isn't that all the more reason, Dr Wells, why Nicola should remain where she is until you have had the opportunity of accurately monitoring the results?'

'That, I'm afraid, would be a total abuse of the remand system. Broadmoor has much better facilities than Holloway does, Mr Owen, and there are doctors there who are well qualified to treat Nicola under proper clinical conditions.'

The heart that had leapt now hit the floor.

'I must go now,' Dr Wells said, 'but we're meeting on the . . .'

'Seventeenth,' Ed reminded him. 'That's the date we agreed when we spoke on Friday.'

After Dr Wells had rung off, Ed held the telephone receiver for a while before slamming it down and declaring to himself, 'Still *en route* to Broadmoor, are we?' He sucked in two deep breaths to allow his sense of panic to die down. Then he decided to write another letter to Mr Smythe, informing him of what he'd just heard from Dr Wells. Having written, 'I hope that I am not giving the impression that I am clutching at straws,' Ed went on to suggest that serious thought should be given to obtaining

Dr Katharina Dalton as an expert witness on premenstrual syndrome at Nicola's trial.

In reply to the letters he had received from the Owens and the dozen or so sent by friends of Nicola's confirming that her childhood had been a most normal one, Mr Smythe wrote to the Owens, 'I must confess I am rather at a loss at the moment to know how we are going to approach this case. I did have certain views but they may not now necessarily be the right ones.' He went on to say that he had fixed a conference to take place with Mr Giacomo on 9 October because, 'I fear that the case may come into the List at any time and at the moment we seem to be in some disarray.'

Ed was late returning home that evening but, after reading Mr Smythe's letter, he decided to ring his solicitor at his home. Pam tried to dissuade him, but Ed insisted that he must make a quick call about an urgent matter that was concerning him.

'Sorry to break into your private time, Mr Smythe,' Ed said, 'but we were wondering whether we should be trying to make contact with Dr Dalton or whether you feel it's more proper for you to do so.'

'I have the matter in hand, Mr Owen,' Mr Smythe replied a touch wearily. 'Leave it to me.'

'That's fine. So you have agreed that she should be called as an expert witness?'

'I agree that she should be approached, Mr Owen.'

'Excellent. Sorry to bother you, Mr Smythe. Good-night.'

After he'd put the phone down, Mr Smythe gave his wife a tired smile and said, 'That bloody man seems to think he's the only one who can be trusted to do anything.'

Unsmilingly, his wife replied, 'That bloody man doesn't seem to sleep. He's taken to ringing you here at all times of the day and night.'

Mrs Smythe wasn't to know it, but Ed Owen slept better that night than he'd done for many a week.

A few days later, the meeting took place between the Owens and Mr Giacomo at his chambers.

Mr Smythe's clerk was also present. Sitting behind them, he listened carefully and remained silent throughout the discussion.

Mr Giacomo first enquired about Nicola's progress and Ed excitedly reported that she had just been moved from her strip cell back into a normal dormitory.

'You saw Dr Wells. Was it yesterday?' the barrister went on to ask.

'No, Tuesday,' Ed replied.

'What did he have to say?'

Both Pam and Ed started to speak at the same time but after they'd exchanged a quick glance, Pam replied 'He describes Nicola's progress as improved and he's continuing to treat her with a synthetic progesterone. He also talked about the surprising fact that the usual tranquillizer didn't seem to have any effect on Nicola. We gave him all Nicola's school reports to show that she'd had a normal childhood until she was fourteen and he read them with some interest.'

As she paused to think if there was anything else that needed to be reported, Ed jumped in with, 'But he said he'd made a further application for her transfer to Broadmoor. He thinks that because of her need for suitable care and treatment, it is an abuse of the remand system for her to be in Holloway. He says that he doesn't want to see her there when he returns from holiday in a month's time.'

Choosing not to comment on this, Mr Giacomo peered at them over the top of his spectacles and went on, 'I've read your letters, Mr Owen, and the magazine article. Nicola's behaviour pattern and the link with her menstrual cycle are extremely interesting. Have you managed to get hold of this Dr Dalton?'

'Mr Smythe said he would do that.'

'Oh!' Mr Giacomo exclaimed, putting down the fountain pen he was holding and turning over the pages of the bulky file before him. 'I can't see any mention of it here.' Pulling a clean sheet of paper from the small wad to his left, he quickly wrote a few words. 'I'll have a word with Mr Smythe about that.' Then he leant back in his chair and removed his spectacles.

Ed started to speak, but Mr Giacomo motioned him to wait. Then, choosing his words with care, he said, 'I am in some difficulty with this case. Having read the documentation and evidence that I have before me, I am of the opinion that it would be best for Nicola to be transferred from the penal system into the medical system. There is no doubt in my mind that she needs medical help and the medical help she needs is not available in prison.'

Slowly and deliberately, Ed replied, 'Mr Giacomo, we would rather have Nicola in prison than locked away, perhaps for ever, in a lunatic asylum. We think that prisons are more accessible than those places. Our daughter isn't mad and we think her illness is medical and not mental. Her improvement in Holloway over the last few weeks has been quite amazing.'

'You do realize, Mr Owen, that Nicola could be sent to prison for ten to fifteen years. She's a double arsonist and, according to the psychiatric reports, a dangerous person. The judge has a responsibility to protect property and the lives of others. What else do you think he can do?'

The horrific spectre of Nicola receiving a sentence of between ten and fifteen years in prison momentarily silenced Ed, but Pam said, 'We know, Mr Giacomo, what the judge will do, unless we can provide the medical evidence to prove that Nicola can be cured. To do this, it may be necessary for Nicola to stay for some time in a medical hospital.'

'And that, Mrs Owen, is our problem,' Mr Giacomo said, clasping his hands together almost as though he was praying. 'We know of no medical hospital that is secure. The judge may well agree with you that Nicola's illness is more medical than mental but, given the fact that until the illness is cured Nicola is considered to present a danger to herself and others, any establishment in which she is treated must be a secure one. You do understand, don't you? Broadmoor has medical as well as psychiatric facilities. It is also a secure hospital. We all agree that Nicola needs medical treatment. Under the circumstances, I feel there is no alternative but for me to endeavour to obtain her release from the penal system.'

'So you want to plead her case on the grounds of insanity?' Ed demanded.

'Yes. I do not think there is any other option unless . . .' He paused and readjusted his spectacles. 'Unless we can produce medical evidence to confirm that Nicola can be successfully treated without secure confinement. It's a tall order.'

'But the article says that premenstrual syndrome can . . . is being cured in a hospital clinic,' Pam protested.

'Quite so. But as yet, Mrs Owen, we have no medical evidence that premenstrual syndrome is the major cause of Nicola's problems. That is why I am convinced of the need for further medical facts. But I must make myself clear. Should we decide to go down that path, it is one of considerable risk. The case will be presented with no alternative but to leave her in the penal system and, if we fail to convince the judge, Nicola will go to prison for a very long time. Is that a risk you are prepared to take?'

'Not at this moment of time it isn't, Mr Giacomo,' Ed said firmly. 'That decision should be taken when, and only when, we've obtained all the medical facts. That's what we're trying to do.'

Mr Giacomo quickly scanned through the papers in front of him before saying, 'We haven't yet been advised that the case is listed, but I suspect it soon will be. I think we must seek an adjournment immediately. If we are successful, we may just be given the time we need.'

# CHAPTER NINETEEN

## *Gatecrashers*

After spending just over five weeks in the strip cell, it was wonderful to be back in the psychiatric unit. Although at times I was a little unhappy and worried, my depression seemed to have vanished completely. I felt much more in control of myself and the routine of prison life seemed to help me. I even started to think of the consequences before I did anything.

It seemed that the hormone pill I was being given was really helping me. I even stopped fearing what the next day might bring. For the first time since all my problems had begun, I knew that I wasn't mad and that there was every chance that, when I was released from prison, I would be able at last to live a normal life.

Of course, I still had some problems. I was overweight and found it extremely difficult not to gorge myself whenever I had the opportunity. The officers did what they could to help. I was constantly being put on special diets and a wardress gave me a notice to stick on my wall which said, 'Think thin'. I tried, but the mirror told me it wasn't working!

I was no longer obsessed by the belief that if I lost weight all my troubles would be over. There was no need. It was the hormone pills rather than a successful diet that seemed to be sorting out most of my problems.

The better I began to feel, the more I thought about my family and how much my parents had done for me.

In the prison chapel one Sunday, the vicar spoke about forgiveness. A disciple asked, 'Jesus, how many times do we forgive – seven times?' Jesus replied, 'No, seventy times seven times.'

It struck me so forcibly then how Mum and Dad had stood by me and forgiven me so many times. I don't think I'd have been able to survive without their wonderful letters and visits during the previous three months. Every day, I ached inside to be with them and share my thoughts with them. I was constantly aware of how much I loved them and of how much their love meant to me.

Being back in the main prison, I was regularly reminded how fortunate I was compared to so many of the other prisoners. There was a special unit to wean addicts off drugs where there were many incredibly skinny girls who were constantly shaking and had heavy black circles under their eyes. There was another unit for the women who were pregnant when they came into prison. They were usually allowed to keep their babies with them for only six months after birth. The infants were then sent to foster parents until their mothers were released from prison. It was so sad to see these young mothers wheeling crying babies around in their prams within the confines of a prison. There was also a lot of lesbianism in Holloway and it was common to see two girls kissing and touching each other. I could understand it, because all of the prisoners so badly wanted affection.

A microcosm of female society, Holloway contained all kinds of women from nervous seventeen year olds who'd been sent there for a week because they'd been caught shoplifting to violently aggressive criminals who'd think nothing of mugging an old woman for a few pence. There were also pathetic old drunks and well-educated middle-class ladies who seemed totally out of place.

One of these was Louise. Always seeming very arrogant, she was slim and regal. I discovered that one day she had returned home and found her husband in bed with a friend. So she stabbed him to death. Then, in hysterics, she rushed to the police station and reported what she had done. The duty sergeant didn't believe her and told her to go back home and calm down. An hour later, Louise returned to the police station and plonked a Sainsbury's carrier-bag on to the counter. Inside was her husband's head.

Then there was Anna who, it was said, had been to university and was a librarian. She was always very pleasant but there was something about her that seemed a little edgy, as though she was only just managing to keep in check her obvious violent streak. But she had a wonderful voice. Every evening when we had been locked into our cells, she would start to sing. Then, for once, the prison would become still and everybody would listen quietly as the beautiful melody of her favourite song, 'Plaisir d'Amour', echoed around the wing. As you listened to her, it was difficult to remember that she was in Holloway facing a murder charge. A kleptomaniac, one day she'd walked into a shop which was being refitted. As it was one o'clock, the workmen had gone off for their lunch. Seeing that the shop was fairly empty, Anna picked up a piece of jewellery and put it into her pocket. A shop assistant saw her and challenged her. Anna grabbed a workman's hammer and smashed it into the shop assistant's skull twenty-six times.

Every prisoner had a story and I listened to many of them as I followed my new routine of leaving the cell as often as possible. On Sunday, I went to chapel. Every day, there were three visits to the dining-room and, on weekday afternoons, I went to occupational therapy, where, because of my injured hand, I did a lot of left-handed painting. I also started Spanish and A level English lessons. In addition, I fitted in a few yoga and dance classes. These convinced me that my dancing was a thing of the past. I simply didn't enjoy it any more.

I found that the early mornings were the worst. Every day, for a few seconds after I woke, I'd think it had all been a dreadful nightmare, but then the terrible realization of what had happened dawned on me and, for a few minutes, I'd feel absolutely shattered.

Yet it wasn't being in prison that upset me. That was safe and secure. It was because I had very mixed feelings about returning to the outside world. On the one hand, I was dying to do something constructive with my life, something worthwhile that I enjoyed. On the other hand, I was filled with great trepidation. What if I failed my parents again? What if I couldn't cope?

I thought a lot about my parents and the great efforts they were making on my behalf. Much of the time when I was locked in my cell was spent rereading the chatty and informative letters they'd sent me. They did so much to cheer me up. In my replies, I tried my best to do the same for them. On 30 October, I finished my letter to Mum and Dad: 'Well, I must go now. I have a lot going on – socializing in Monte Carlo, a trip to Rome to do the odd bit of sculpture and then Paris for the odd daub on canvas before I return to a jammed switchboard with calls from Paul (Newman), Ryan (O'Neal), Oliver (Reed) and Frank (Sinatra) who insists on singing down the phone. It's better than Butlin's here, you know.'

*　*　*

On 4 November, the Owens received the Counsel's Opinion that Mr Giacomo had prepared. In it, he painstakingly gave the reasons why, in his view, all the necessary medical reports should be obtained before the hearing of the case.

Two days later, Pam telephoned Ed at a client's office, 'Mr Smythe has just rung,' she said. 'We're at the Old Bailey tomorrow—'

'The trial!' he interrupted. 'It's not the trial, for heaven's sake?'

'No. We've got our hearing for the adjournment.'

234

Ed was over the moon. 'Good old Mr Smythe! It's great news! Look, I've just a couple of things to tidy up here and then I'll leave for home. It's marvellous news!'

Pam was not so certain. All that had happened was that they'd obtained a hearing – not the adjournment.

The following day, Ed and Pam travelled up to London by train and took a taxi to the Old Bailey, arriving just before nine o'clock. As they were about to enter the imposing entrance hall, they were stopped by a sturdy policeman who wanted to know what they were there for, who they were and the name of their barrister. Having satisfied him, Ed and Pam hurried down the hall to Mr Giacomo, who was peering at a notice on the wall.

After they'd exchanged greetings, Mr Giacomo said, pointing to the door of a court, 'This is where we are.' He then glanced back at the notice. 'We'll be the fifth to be called. I should think that will be about eleven o'clock.' He opened the door just sufficiently to peep inside. Then he added, 'It looks as though the first case is just about to start. You might like to go in and watch the proceedings. It'll help you understand what will take place when we present our plea.'

Before either of them could reply, Mr Giacomo greeted Mr Smythe's clerk who was hurrying towards them carrying a thin wallet of papers. Taking this from him, Mr Giacomo opened it, removed several documents and quickly leafed through them. 'Did Mr Smythe contact Dr Dalton?' he asked the clerk. 'There's no mention of it here,' he added, jabbing the file with the knuckles of his clenched fist.

'Mr Smythe didn't say anything to me when I collected the papers first thing this morning.'

Mr Giacomo pushed his wig up from over the left ear and slowly scratched the hair close to his temple. He looked a trifle irritated.

Sensing that he wanted to have some more words with Mr Smythe's clerk, Ed and Pam left and quietly entered the court where they sat down close to the door. After they'd seen the judge turn down three applications for bail in quick succession, they left the court and rejoined Mr Giacomo.

With a wry smile, he asked, 'Well, what do you think of the learned judge?'

'He's a bit irascible,' Ed replied, 'but at least he gets on with it. Do you know him?'

Mr Giacomo shook his head and said, with emphasis, 'Only by reputation.'

As Ed and Pam were exchanging concerned glances, Mr Smythe's clerk rushed out of the court and announced, 'We're on.'

They all entered together. Mr Giacomo pointed to some seats and whispered to Pam, 'Don't worry!' Then he threaded his way between benches towards the front table beneath the raised bench where the judge sat, reading some papers.

After a few minutes, the judge looked up and said, 'You may commence, counsel!'

Mr Giacomo outlined Nicola's situation. Although he was succinct and comprehensive, the judge frequently interrupted him.

'Hormones! Did I hear that correctly?' he asked sharply at one point.

'Yes,' Mr Giacomo replied before continuing, 'In France, premenstrual tension is officially recognized by the courts.'

'We're not in France, counsel,' the judge again interrupted. 'I wouldn't have thought there was any need to remind you that this is an English court.'

Things were not going well.

Ed was then called to the stand and sworn in. The judge sat back in his chair and stared at the ceiling as though he couldn't bear to see what was going on in his court.

Ed had only just started to answer questions about the links between Nicola's behaviour and her menstrual cycle, when the judge leant forward and barked, 'Who is this woman, Dr Katharina Dalton? Is she in court?'

'I understand that my solicitor has had some difficulty in contacting her,' Ed replied weakly.

At this, the judge turned to Mr Giacomo and said, 'If this woman is essential to your case, she should be here. In any event, if further medical evidence is required, let the learned judge who hears the case decide. It may well be myself! Let this young woman be brought to trial. Application for adjournment is refused.'

Outside the court, amidst the august splendour of the marbled hall, the Owens rejoined their barrister. Mr Giacomo was furious. He pushed back his wig. 'Forgive me for saying this, Mrs Owen. But that man . . . That man is an absolute f...!' he exclaimed.

The prospect of Nicola's case being heard by that judge was too much for Pam. She burst into tears.

His fury unabated, Mr Giacomo turned on her and snapped, 'You're no good to me like that, Mrs Owen. You're no help to Nicola either. If you can't stand the heat in the kitchen, then you must leave!'

Pam's tears stopped immediately.

'What do you want us to do, Mr Giacomo?' Ed asked. 'We're ready to do anything we possibly can.'

'Get hold of Dr Dalton and do it right now. There's not a minute to be lost.'

Taking him at his word, Ed and Pam hurried out of the Old Bailey and at the corner of Newgate Street managed to hail a taxi to take them to University College Hospital.

The receptionist there was apologetic. 'I'm afraid Dr Dalton doesn't have a clinic here today,' she said.

'But we must speak with her today. It's most urgent,' Ed declared.

'Well, I'm sure she does have a private patients' clinic in Harley Street today.'

'What number in Harley Street?'

'I'll look it up for you,' the receptionist replied and rushed into a small cubicle of an office where she sifted through a stack of battered yellow cards. Pulling one out, she returned. 'This is it,' she announced. '88 Harley Street. And, yes, I'm right. She does have her private patients' clinic there today.'

A taxi took them to 88 Harley Street. They bounded up the steps and pressed the brass bell button. As if by remote control, the exceptionally wide door opened and a woman in a white uniform appeared.

'We've come to see Dr Dalton,' Ed announced.

'There's no-one by that name here, I'm afraid,' the woman in white replied.

Ed and Pam stared at each other in disbelief. 'Look,' Ed said angrily. 'The University College Hospital has just given us this number as the place where Dr Dalton has her private clinic.'

'I'm sorry, but I've already told you that there's no doctor of that name practising at this address.'

Pam wasn't prepared to wait any longer. She skipped down the steps to look elsewhere, but Ed persisted. 'She's an eminent doctor who specializes in premenstrual tension. Articles about her work appear in magazines. I think she's written books about it. You must have heard of her!'

'I've found it,' Pam suddenly shouted from the bottom of the flight of steps. 'She's next door. It's number 86.'

'Sorry to have bothered you,' Ed declared to the bemused-looking woman before running down the steps to join his wife.

At number 86, another door opened to reveal yet another woman resplendent in her crisp, white uniform.

'We're here to see Dr Dalton,' Ed declared.

'Please come in.'

In the hallway, the nurse asked, 'Who shall I say is wishing to see her?'

Ed couldn't remember the judge's name and so he invented one. 'We have been directed to come here by Judge

238

Griffiths of the Old Bailey. It's a matter of considerable importance. We are Mr and Mrs Owen.'

The nurse looked Ed up and down as he stood there in his immaculate black pin-striped suit. Deciding that he wasn't an imposter or an escaped lunatic, she said, 'I won't be a minute.' She wasn't. Returning almost immediately, she said, 'Dr Dalton will see you right away.' Then she directed them to the stairs that led down to Dr Dalton's basement surgery.

As they entered, a large woman, wearing a simple print dress with half sleeves, stood up behind her desk. 'Mr and Mrs Owen?' They nodded. 'I'm Dr Dalton. I understand you've just come from the Old Bailey?' she said in a clear, yet husky, voice that had just the hint of a lisp as though a peppermint was being held under the tongue.

'We have.'

'So tell me what Sara's been up to?'

'Our daughter's name is Nicola!' Ed corrected her.

Dr Dalton glanced down at the file on her desk. It was clearly labelled Sara Owen. She looked at them with some bewilderment. 'Am I to take it then that you are not Sara Owen's parents?'

'No, we are not.'

'Well, who are you?' Dr Dalton asked. 'And what are you doing gatecrashing my private clinic?'

'Dr Dalton, if you would be so good as to give us just two minutes of your time, I will explain,' Ed said. 'We apologize for this gross intrusion but it is a matter of grave importance.'

Dr Dalton sat back down in her chair, clasped her hands together with her arms resting on the desk. 'Two minutes, Mr Owen!'

The Owens sat down on the edges of the chairs that had been offered to them and, as Dr Dalton watched Ed's face carefully, he gave a brief account of Nicola's problems and the reasons why it seemed as though these were caused by premenstrual syndrome. 'We're in a terrible situation,' he concluded. 'If a plea of insanity is accepted, Nicola will be sent to Broadmoor. Yet if the plea is entered that she is suffering from a medical illness and this is not accepted, through lack of adequate medical evidence, Nicola will be given a very long prison sentence.'

When he had finished, Dr Dalton asked quietly, 'Mr and Mrs Owen, what do you want me to do for your daughter?'

Pam responded quickly. 'My husband and I want to know if you would be prepared to testify as an expert witness at our daughter's trial.'

'Mrs Owen, please don't ask me to do that. I could be sitting at the Old Bailey for any number of days waiting to be called. What would happen to my poor patients?' She opened a thick appointments diary on her desk and pointed to rows of names. 'Every day, I see as many patients as I can. I want you to understand that for many of them their whole quality of life depends upon following a programme that I have to administer. So I'm afraid it's impossible for me to agree to be an expert witness at any trial.'

'What can you do for our daughter, Dr Dalton?' Pam asked with increasing desperation. 'Unless something is done and done soon she will be sent to Broadmoor and we consider that would be a terrible mistake.'

'You're right. It is a horrific prospect for Nicola if, as seems possible, she is a victim of premenstrual syndrome.'

'Then please help us in any way you can,' Pam pleaded, her voice fading almost to a whisper.

'What I can do is to go and see Nicola in Holloway. Can you make arrangements with the prison doctor?'

'Yes,' Ed replied. 'Through the solicitor. But Dr Wells, the chief prison psychiatrist, is away on holiday at the moment. There's a Dr Graham standing in for him.'

Dr Dalton consulted her diary. 'I can see Nicola on 21 November,' she said. 'It will have to be after surgery hours, say at seven in the evening.'

Pam made a note of the date and time.

'Now, Mrs Owen,' Dr Dalton continued. 'I want you to give me a full written account of Nicola's life, illnesses and behaviour since her birth, right up to the present. I want to know all about her achievements as well. As time is so short, you must do it as soon as possible. I will take her blood samples when I see her in Holloway.' For the first time, she glanced at her watch. The promised two minutes had already been much expanded. 'It's unfortunate that Dr Wells is on holiday,' Dr Dalton added thoughtfully. 'I think I know him.'

'Excuse my asking, Dr Dalton,' Pam said. 'But I understand you've written a book about premenstrual syndrome. What is its title? We'd like to buy a copy and we also thought it'd be a good idea to send a copy of it to the barrister, the solicitor and the psychiatrists involved in Nicola's case.'

'It is a good idea, Mrs Owen. The book you might find most useful is called *Once a Month*, although I would suggest that for Dr Wells you acquire another of my books called *Premenstrual Syndrome and Progesterone Therapy*. It's rather more technical and it may prove more useful to him.' Dr Dalton then stood up and, as she showed them out of the surgery, her final words were, 'Don't forget, Mrs Owen. I need that report as soon as possible.'

'It will be done, Dr Dalton. And once again we thank you. Thank you for everything.'

Bubbling with pleasure, Ed and Pam walked quickly from Harley Street to Tottenham Court Road where they managed to buy several copies of Dr Dalton's two books. Then they returned home in the best of spirits.

Ed telephoned Mr Smythe, not to complain about the failure of his solicitor to contact Dr Dalton but to report his own success. Full of enthusiasm, Ed went on to suggest other ways of producing expert evidence. Dr Morley and the probation officer should be asked to see Nicola again so they could assess for themselves the dramatic changes that had taken place. Dr Sangster should also be approached. As a hospital consultant, he had known Nicola for nearly eighteen months.

Mr Smythe promised to contact all of them, but he also sounded a warning note. 'You have to realize, Mr Owen, that the case against Nicola could be called very shortly. As the application for an adjournment has been rejected, there is even a possibility that the case might come to trial before Dr Dalton's visit or at least before she's received the results of the blood tests and has had time to write her report.'

Even this possibility could not dispirit Ed. He knew he had a fight on his hands. He'd known that ever since Nicola was sent back to Holloway. But he loved a good fight, especially if he was well prepared. And this time he was doing his damnedest to ensure he had the most expert of seconds in his corner.

# CHAPTER TWENTY

## *Miracles*

Pam spent several days preparing her account of Nicola's life for Dr Dalton. She listed Nicola's illnesses, checked through the school reports and unearthed certificates that Nicola had been awarded. After she'd finished the draft report, she read it over to Ed so that he could provide missing information. She asked Sally questions and spoke to Johnnie when he phoned.

Having gathered all the information, she sat down to type the final version. Then she carefully read through the ten double-spaced pages to check for any errors. When these had been corrected, she decided she must read the whole of her report to Ed. So she went upstairs to the bedroom where he lay fast asleep.

Shaking his shoulder, she exclaimed proudly, 'I've done it, Ed. It's finished! Wake up! Ed, wake up! It's all done. I want to read it to you!'

'What's that?' he mumbled, his eyes refusing to open.

'I've finished it. I just want to read it over to you.'

'What's the time for heaven's sake?' he asked, peering at the alarm clock on the far chest of drawers.

Pam glanced at her watch. 'It's twenty past four in the morning,' she said brightly.

Slowly coming to, he said, 'Never mind the time. What day is it?'

'It was Wednesday when you went to bed and now it's

Thursday. It's too dark to see but I'm sure it's going to be a lovely day.'

When Ed was securely propped up in bed, Pam read him her story of their daughter's life. When she'd finished, exhausted but contented, she climbed into bed and instantly fell fast asleep. Ed, on the other hand, was wide awake. He felt far too excited and optimistic to slumber. So he opted for getting up and making a cup of tea.

In the kitchen, he shared some digestive biscuits with Emma who happily gobbled up the unexpected treat. Hoping for more, she followed Ed into the office and flopped down by the side of the desk as he wrote a covering letter for Pam's report to Dr Dalton. When this was finished, he went into the sitting-room to check whether any glasses or cups needed to be collected and stacked in the dishwasher. Surprised at how tidy the room was, he went upstairs and took a shower. Afterwards, he stole back into the bedroom and, as silently as he could, collected some clothes. With a pair of trousers over his right arm, a sweater in one hand and his socks and underwear in the other, and his shoes lodged tightly under his armpits, he tiptoed out and went into Johnnie's empty bedroom. After he'd dressed, he went downstairs, collected Emma and set off for a walk in Bexley Woods just as the sky was beginning to lighten.

Prompted by Pam's account, memories of Nicola came flooding back to him as he walked. He vividly recalled the day when she was first brought home from the hospital where she was born. In the afternoon, she'd been put in her pram on the back lawn. A little while later, when he went out to see her, he had the biggest shock of his life – not a metre from the pram was the biggest rat he'd ever seen. He went after it like a bat out of hell.

Standing for a while on the river bank, Ed gazed at the rippling water. It hardly seemed any time ago that, one warm June evening, he'd stood there watching an excited young Nicola catching her first fish.

*Look, Daddy. Look, look! I've really caught a fish!*

Turning away, Ed called Emma and briskly walked back up the hill. Rather than awaken Pam, he prepared Sally a breakfast of cereal and boiled eggs and then drove her to school. By the time he returned, the post had arrived.

He selected the letter from his solicitor that he had been waiting for and impatiently ripped it open. A compliment slip was attached by a paper-clip to photocopies of letters from Dr Morley and Dr Sangster. He read them with increasing excitement and dashed upstairs.

'Pam! Wake up, wake up!' he called. 'It's great news, absolutely great!'

Pam was awake in an instant. 'What good news?' she asked. 'From whom?'

'Just listen to these two letters that have been sent to Smythe. The first one's from Dr Morley . . .'

He read the whole of the letter, which acknowledged the incredible change that had taken place in Nicola's appearance and attitude since she had been treated with Duphaston, the synthetic progesterone. Dr Morley said that he was delighted that Nicola was to be seen by Dr Dalton and concluded, 'I am too long in the tooth to be over-impressed with "miracles", and I would like to see her improvement maintained for, say, six months. I would also like to consider Dr Dalton's opinion as to the feasibility of the clinical change in her being attributable to the hormone therapy. If she is positive that improvement is caused by the hormonal treatment, then the prognosis becomes infinitely better and the disposal much easier. In other words, if Nicola can now be considered safe, then it would be feasible to go to the court and ask for her to be placed on probation with a condition of surveillance by a probation officer and continued treatment with hormones.'

'Ed,' Pam exclaimed, 'he's saying it's a miracle.'

'That's what it is – a bloody miracle. But now listen to what Dr Sangster has to say.'

Once again, Ed read the whole letter, which expressed

the view that the final disposition in Nicola's case should not be made until it had been established whether her behaviour problems were 'hormone dependent'. The letter also contained information that up till then had been unknown to Ed and Pam: 'Some eight months ago, I was so much impressed by the relationship with Nicola's behaviour to her menses that I asked one of my gynaecological colleagues to see Nicola. A course of hormones was prescribed but unfortunately, for reasons quite beyond the patient's control and indeed mine, she was given the drug for only a few days and no valid conclusions could be drawn as to whether, had she continued with it in the prescribed manner, it would have been helpful or not.'

'I'm not sure what that's all about,' Pam said.

'Well, I know,' Ed said bitterly. 'That bloody psychiatrist, Dr Goble, stopped the course of hormone treatment so he could give Nicola those bloody big doses of tranquillizers. That's what it's all about. If he hadn't interfered, Nicola wouldn't be in Holloway now.'

'Ed, stop it! He did what he thought was right.'

'Listen to me, Pam—'

'No, Ed Owen, you listen to me,' Pam interrupted, only slightly raising her voice. 'We've had really good news this morning. There's real hope now. There's nothing to be gained by looking back. Please, don't spoil it.'

It took a moment for Ed's temper to abate. 'You're right. I'm sorry,' he said and went downstairs to make the tea.

Sitting up in bed, Pam reflected on what was happening. The change in Dr Morley's professional opinion was almost as miraculous as the change that had taken place in Nicola. Things certainly seemed to have turned the corner, but there was still a long way to go. Pam felt too uncertain to be really happy. Until Dr Dalton had carried out her tests, nothing could be certain.

Yet, even though Nicola was in prison, those three months had allowed order and normality to be re-established in the Owen household. The tension that had been building up over the last four years had dissipated. Ed had stopped shouting and was able to reason again. Freed from the unbearable restraint of having constantly to keep watch on Nicola, Pam had slowly recovered her own equilibrium and no longer needed daily doses of tranquillizers. After years of being preoccupied by Nicola, Ed and Pam had also been able to spend more of their time and energy on Sally and Johnnie. More than it had been for many a year, the Owen family was united and lacked only Nicola's return.

Or so it seemed. But by accepting that there was at least a possibility that Nicola might come home, Pam had to face the question that up to then had been all to easy to ignore – did she really want Nicola back again? As soon as the question was framed, Pam knew both the answer and why she had previously been afraid to ask it. The question had been unnecessary only because Nicola couldn't return home unless a suitable treatment for her had been discovered. The possibility that she might return depended on a cure being found. This meant that the Nicola that did return home would be the old Nicola, not the sick and unpredictable Nicola that had turned her mother's life into a horrendous nightmare.

'Of course I want her back!' Pam said aloud, pleased at having picked her way though such a convoluted argument with herself.

Two days later, on 18 November, Pam went with Sally to visit Nicola. There was never time during those all too brief meetings to say the things that really mattered and so afterwards Pam decided to put down her thoughts in a letter to Nicola. 'We all really love you, Nicola,' she said, 'but we too are in need of help and when you do come home, which I am sure will be sooner than we think, it will be as a girl with the resolve, determination and health to help us all get our super family unit back to an even better key than before. As a mum, I know that I need you as a friend and, although I will do all I

247

can to help you, I can no longer be your keeper. It's age, Babe!'

On Tuesday, 21 November – the day that Dr Dalton was to visit Nicola – the Owens received a letter from her. After Ed had read it, he called to Pam who was in the bathroom washing her hair, 'Pam, we've had a reply from Dr Dalton. You'll need to look at it straight away.'

He went back to the office and reread the letter. After a few minutes, Pam appeared in his bathrobe, with a towel wrapped around her head. She took the letter and read it quickly. Looking up in astonishment, she exclaimed, 'Good gracious! She wants about twenty-five dates covering a period . . .' she paused and quickly skimmed through part of the letter. 'Dates covering a period of about five years.'

'That's right,' Ed replied, picking up an open copy of Dr Dalton's book. 'And it's all in here. It seems from this as if the preparation of a menstrual chart is more important than the blood testing. Handing her the book, he went on, 'You can read it for yourself. The dates she wants from us are vitally important and it seems to me that unless we come up with them we can kiss goodbye to any hope of her making a diagnosis let alone a prognosis.'

Pam sat down at the typing desk and read the paragraphs Ed had pointed out, as he went quietly through the rest of the mail. When she'd finished reading, she said, 'You're right. We've got to do it right away. The problem is knowing where to start.'

'Well, there're my business diaries over there in the bookcase that go back a few years. Unfortunately, I've thrown all my personal diaries away, but you've kept yours, haven't you?'

Pam nodded. 'They may be some help, but I think the best thing to do is to phone up all the doctors who've been involved to see if any of the dates Dr Dalton wants are in their medical records. We'll also have to contact the hospitals that have treated Nicola. Let's see,' Pam said, checking the list of questions, 'she wants to know the dates of admission into the various hospitals when Nicola had taken an overdose, had peritonitis, had amnesia, took weed-killer, cut her face with a razor, had a stomach-pump and when she cut her wrists. That's eight of the twenty-three dates she wants.'

'And there's the police station,' Ed added helpfully. 'They'll have some more of the dates.'

'Yes, they will,' Pam said, again checking the letter, 'but there's only a couple of things, like Nicola breaking her bail by staying out all night. Anyway, don't you worry about it. You're going to be late for your meeting in Reigate. So off you go. Leave it to me. I'll sort it out.'

Reminded of his appointment, Ed left hurriedly and, as soon as she'd dried her hair and dressed, Pam started her long round of telephone calls. Only a couple of people were obstructive and in both cases Pam managed to find out the information she required from other sources. At both the hospitals, clerks said that they couldn't give information about patients over the telephone. So, in the afternoon, Pam had to drive to the two hospitals.

In addition to asking the dates of events involving Nicola, Dr Dalton also wanted to know about both Pam's and Sally's periods. So, later on in the day, Pam tried to sort out with her daughter the date of Sally's first menstruation. For Nicola, it had been easy enough and the actual day was soon tracked down, but for Sally it was very different. Pam was disturbed to discover that, not only could neither of them work out the date, they couldn't even remember whether Sally was twelve or thirteen at the time.

At twenty to eight that evening, when Ed returned home, Pam was still collating information. Later, by searching through the almost illegible entries in Ed's pocket diary, they were both delighted to be able to add two more dates to the list.

Both were exhausted when, for once, they decided that an early night would do them the power of good.

They slept through the alarm call and it was well past eight before Ed clambered out of bed. He was irritated. Always an early riser, there was nothing more calculated to ruin his day than getting up late. He was even more irritated when he went downstairs and discovered that the post had already arrived. It was yet another reminder of how late he was.

He picked up the assorted envelopes and took them into the kitchen where first he filled the kettle and laid the breakfast tray. Then, as was his custom, he arranged the letters in what he deemed to be the order of priority. The first one he read was from Mr Smythe. It puzzled him.

Pam was already awake when he brought the tea to the bedroom. Sitting on the edge of the bed, with the tray balanced on his knees, Ed handed the solicitor's letter to his wife. As they both sipped their tea in silence, she read it carefully, stopping several times to reread various sections. Watching her carefully, Ed was unsure whether to be pleased or disappointed that she appeared to be as puzzled as he was.

'I think it's good news, Ed,' she said hesitantly, handing the letter back to Ed. 'What do you think?'

'Well, there is some good news. He says that the case won't be heard before 18 December and so that gives us just over three more weeks. But, apart from that, the letter has far too many ifs and maybes for my liking,' Ed replied. 'For example, Smythe says, "It is to be hoped that the medical evidence or reports are of such a nature that they can persuade the court that there will be no further risks either to Nicola or anyone else if a non-custodial sentence is given. It may on the other hand be that Dr Dalton will recommend that treatment is given in a controlled environment or possibly even whilst Nicola is in custody." In other words, anything can happen.'

'But that's true – at the moment. Come on, Eddie. Be reasonable. All he's really saying is that Dr Dalton's report is crucial because the court's likely to go along with whatever she recommends.'

'Well, Dr Dalton saw Nicola yesterday and so we won't have to wait long for her report.'

'We will if I don't get on,' Pam declared, climbing out of bed. 'I really must get cracking. Even when I've tracked down the last couple of dates, I've still got to type it all up.'

Ed smiled admiringly at his wife. Himself a man of action, he loved to see others getting on with things. It was the people who just sat on their bottoms and did nothing to help themselves that he despised.

\*　　\*　　\*

I wasn't very happy to be told that I was going to be visited by yet another specialist. It seemed to me that it would just prolong the case and I was getting sick and tired of not knowing what was going to happen to me. I'd even reached the stage when I didn't really care what decision was made as long as something was actually decided.

When Mum and Dad visited me, they explained that the specialist was Dr Dalton, who was an important gynaecologist and a leading authority on premenstrual problems. That made me feel much better, because I certainly didn't want to see yet another psychiatrist or take any more of their drugs. They seemed to have made me worse instead of better. But I did enjoy seeing Dr Morley again when he visited me. He was very kind and told me that it was beginning to seem unlikely that I would be sent to Broadmoor. That really cheered me up.

The main trouble was that Mum and Dad didn't seem to let me know what was going on. They kept on giving me snippets of information. They'd seen this person and that person, made dozens of telephone calls and written stacks of letters. Perhaps they didn't want to build my hopes up unnecessarily and I did know how hard they were

251

working on my behalf, but I still couldn't help feeling that I seemed to be the last person who knew what was going to happen to me.

Because of this, I wrote to Dad asking if I could meet Mr Giacomo. It didn't seem too much to ask for me to meet my own barrister. As it was, I didn't even know if I was expected to plead guilty or whether I'd have to go into the witness-box. That was something I certainly wanted to do. I felt it was important that the judge knew my feelings.

Another problem I had was that, although the hormone treatment seemed to be working and I no longer had the depressing thoughts that had so often possessed me, it didn't cover up the terrible guilt and remorse that I felt. I really couldn't understand why I had done so many terrible things – why I'd taken those overdoses, run away from home, shaved off my hair, and set fire to our beautiful house.

I was pleased to be able to discuss these feelings and problems with Katharina Dalton when she came to visit me. I was really impressed by her. She was easy to talk to and I felt very comfortable with her.

She asked me what effect alcohol had on me and I told her it depended on my mood. If I was happy, alcohol made me happier, but if I was depressed it made me feel even worse.

'Do you know when a period is coming?' she wanted to know.

'Every time.'

'How do you know?'

'Do you mean now or in the past?'

'Well, let's deal with the past first.'

'That's easy. For a few days before, I felt depressed, I was tense with severe headaches, backache and, even sometimes, nose bleeds. As soon as my period started, my depression lifted and all my pains went away.'

'And now?'

'It's difficult to say. I've only had one period since I was put on the Duphaston pills, but I do know that since I started taking them I haven't suffered at all from depression.'

Katharina Dalton then wanted to know the exact dates when certain things happened. I was quite surprised – and so was she – how many of them I could remember. What was more remarkable was how so many things that had happened tied in with my menstrual cycle. The first time I set fire to the house was the day before my period started. So was the second time. Both the times when I broke a condition of my bail by staying out all night and when I slashed my wrists in prison were a few days before the start of a period. It seemed as if pieces of a jigsaw were being fitted together.

After Katharina Dalton had gone, I spent a long time thinking about the consequences of being able to link my behaviour to my menstrual cycle. In the past, it had been all too easy for me to blame other people for the way I felt and to hit out at them, especially Mum. For the first time, I saw what she had really gone through and I hated myself for it. Of one thing I was sure. I'd never again deliberately make her go through the hell I'd made her endure during the previous four years.

\*　　\*　　\*

On Saturday, 25 November, Ed and Pam went with Sally to visit Nicola. As soon as they returned home, Pam went into the office to type up the answers to Dr Dalton's questions. Sally and Ed went into the kitchen to make the coffee and sandwiches.

'Nicola won't be going to Broadmoor now, will she, Dad?' Sally asked, full of concern.

'I have to be straight with you, Sally, and say that I don't know. All I can say is that Dr Wells is back on Monday and I think he's in for a big surprise. Well, at least I hope he is! Just before he left for his holiday, he made application for Nicola's transfer to Broadmoor and told her that he didn't expect to find her still in Holloway when he returned.'

'But she's absolutely normal, Dad. Look at her this afternoon. She was even starting to have a moan and I can't think of anything more normal than that!'

Ed smiled. 'The old Nicola certainly seems to be back,' he said, 'but I'm afraid that at the moment everything depends on Dr Dalton and her report.'

'And when do you expect to hear from her?'

'Very soon, Sally, although she can't complete her report until she's seen Mum's list of dates.'

Sally was quick to notice her father's face suddenly crease with pain. 'What's the matter, Dad?' she asked.

'My back's killing me. I think I'm going to lie down for a bit.'

'Shall I make you a hot-water bottle?' Sally asked, looking extremely worried.

'Thanks.'

'But what's wrong with your back, Dad?'

'The doctor says it's a tilted pelvis. All I know is it's bloody painful.'

'That's funny, Dad. Wasn't Nicola once told she had a tilted pelvis?'

'Come to think of it, Sal, I'm sure you're right.'

'Well,' she said with a grin, 'perhaps it's your hormones! I think you're just going to have to give up squash, Dad.'

'There's no need,' Ed replied as he made his way out of the kitchen. 'It's giving me up!'

# CHAPTER TWENTY-ONE

## *Race for Life*

Ed left the house early on Monday morning for a meeting in central London. He'd been long gone when the post arrived and so it was Pam who opened a letter from the solicitor, saying, 'I would like one of you to please telephone me if you would, so that I can have a short word about certain matters.'

Pam rang immediately.

'Good morning, Mrs Owen. It was good of you to respond so quickly,' Mr Smythe said. 'And how is Nicola?'

Pam told him about Nicola's continuing progress, adding that her reply to Dr Dalton had been posted that morning.

'I understood that Dr Dalton has just gone away for a few days' holiday.'

Pam's stomach churned over. Despite the speed at which she'd worked, she'd replied too late. 'Do you know when she'll be back?' she asked nervously.

'Just a moment. I have a letter from her . . . Yes, she'll be back on 4 December. Let me just look at my diary. Yes, it's a Monday and so she'll be back a week today.'

Pam felt relieved. She wasn't too late after all. There was still time for Dr Dalton to write her report before Nicola's trial. That couldn't happen for several weeks.

'Now, Mrs Owen, Mr Giacomo wants to see Nicola and I have some dates for you. Hopefully, one of them is convenient for either you or Mr Owen to attend. I'm afraid it will be an evening visit.'

'Mr Owen has business meetings all this week,' Pam replied, 'and so it will be me that goes along. I'll fit in with any evening that suits Mr Giacomo.'

'It's not for this week, but the week after. The first date he has suggested is Monday, 4 December . . . Oh! that's the same day Dr Dalton returns. What a coincidence! Anyway, given the situation, I think if it's at all possible for you, then it would be advisable to go for that date.'

'That's fine. What time do you suggest?'

'Provisionally 6.30 p.m., but I'll come back to you on that after I've had a word with the people at Holloway.'

'That's fine, Mr Smythe. And please thank Mr Giacomo. I know how keen Nicola is to meet him.'

'Yes, indeed. And Mr Giacomo very much wants to have a word with her. I suspect that at the moment he hasn't quite made up his mind about how best to handle the case. There's just one other thing, Mrs Owen. I'd like to send my clerk along, but I'm afraid he hasn't a car. Is there any possibility that you could pick him up from our office on your way in? I hope you don't mind my asking?'

'Not at all. That's fine and I'll even make sure he's brought back in one piece!'

\* \* \*

It seemed to me as though time was standing still. Although people were still coming and going, nothing really seemed to be happening.

My probation officer visited me. I'd never been able to stand her. She was a real stick in the mud. When I asked her if she was going to write a new report for my trial she said, 'I don't think it'll be necessary. The first report wasn't all that bad!'

I also saw Dr Wells several times. I told him that with my trial coming up I really needed to go on a diet. It was bad enough trying to lose weight with all the stodgy food in prison, but I was also helping a great deal in the kitchen, which put even greater temptation my way. So I asked Dr Wells to give me some slimming pills.

'They won't do any good,' he said. 'I know how difficult dieting can be but, I'm sorry to say, it's only a question of willpower. If you are overeating, Nicola, I'm sure it's because you're concerned about your trial and that's quite a normal thing. So don't let it worry you.'

'And when do you think my trial will be, Dr Wells? Will it be before Christmas? I do so much want to spend Christmas with my family.'

'I'm afraid that I've no idea when the trial will be, but I would be most surprised if it comes up before Christmas. So I wouldn't get my hopes up, if I were you. But things are moving along, Nicola. I've just received a letter from your solicitor asking me to write a report for the trial.'

'Not another!' I exclaimed. 'The poor judge will be weighed down with reports!'

That night, I lay awake till two in the morning, tossing and turning, worrying about my trial and what its outcome would be.

It was something of a relief when Mr Giacomo came to see me with Mum. But he wasn't very reassuring. He said that he was considering the advisability of my pleading not guilty on the grounds that I was suffering from automatism.

'What's that?' I asked.

'Temporary insanity. But I have to say it's a very narrow chance.'

When I asked him what he thought my sentence was likely to be, he said I would get a year or maybe even eighteen months, but the five months I'd already been in prison would count as part of the sentence.

That was very upsetting news. I had so hoped to be home for Christmas.

*　　*　　*

Ed and Pam had always made a special occasion of Christmas. Putting up the decorations was an annual ritual that involved every member of the family for several evenings and most of a weekend. Each of the four Christmas trees was carefully dressed with hundreds of baubles and bows of the appropriate colour, swathes of garlands and a twinkling stream of fairy lights. In the sitting-room, the tree was a tall artificial green spruce decorated with red. In the dining-room, the tree glittered with gold. The shimmering tree in the hall was garlanded with pink. Standing outside in the porch was a natural fir tree that was covered with lanterns.

Ed and Pam discussed for some time whether they should decorate the house as usual for Christmas. Although it seemed likely that Nicola would still be in prison, they decided to go ahead – but not without a sense of guilt – for the sake of Johnnie and Sally.

As all the previous years' Christmas trees and decorations had been destroyed in the fire, new ones had to be bought. And so, after their Saturday visit to Nicola, they left Holloway and headed for Harrods. In the past, for this part of the Christmas ritual, they'd been accompanied by their excited, wide-eyed children. This time, they went alone and made their purchases virtually in silence, and in a most unfestive mood.

When they returned home, Sally helped them unload their Christmas purchases from the boot of the Volvo. Everything was safely stored in the hall, when the telephone rang. It was Mr Smythe.

'Sorry to trouble you so late, Mr Owen,' he said.

'We've troubled you many times, Mr Smythe. Don't think anything of it.'

There was a long silence.

'Are you still there, Mr Smythe?' Ed enquired.

'Yes, Mr Owen. Sorry. I was just looking over Dr Dalton's report. It came in today, but I've only just picked it up from the office and so I've done no more than read quickly through it.'

Ed waited for a moment before asking, 'Is it good news?'

'I think it is,' Mr Smythe said, before answering much more positively, 'Yes, it is.'

Another silence. 'What does the report say?' Ed prompted, worried by his solicitor's apparent reticence.

'Well, the diagnosis is premenstrual syndrome which I don't think will come as a surprise to you.'

'And what did she say about the prognosis?' Ed asked, as both Sally and Pam anxiously huddled round him, trying desperately to overhear what Mr Smythe was saying.

'Let me read you the final paragraph of her report.' There was a rustling of papers, before Mr Smythe cleared his throat and read: ' "Miss Owen has undoubtedly responded well to Duphaston but, in view of the severity of her behavioural changes in the premenstrum, it is essential for treatment to be prolonged for at least a year before reducing the dosage. It is possible that the dosage may need to be increased over the next few months. However, if her treatment is well stabilized, there is every likelihood that her antisocial behaviour will be controlled." '

Ed was disappointed. Certainly, this paragraph didn't contain the recommendation he had been hoping for. 'Does she say anywhere else in the report that the treatment can be administered on an out-patient basis?' he asked.

There was a brief pause before Mr Smythe replied, 'She doesn't appear to have addressed that point. I shall have to talk to her about it, but I suspect the omission has been made because she is herself still undecided.'

'That really worries me, Mr Smythe.'

'I appreciate that, Mr Owen, but let's just look at the positive aspects of this report. First, we have the expert in the field confirming that Nicola's illness is premenstrual syndrome. Second, she states that the illness can be treated and thirdly, in the last line of her report, she refers to the likelihood that her antisocial behaviour will be controlled. I take all that to be very positive, Mr Owen. Yes, very positive. I shall send you a copy of the report first thing on Monday.'

'Thank you. I look forward to reading it.'

'Now there is just one other matter. Mr Giacomo would like another conference and he has suggested 19 December, around five o'clock.'

'Just let me check my diary,' Ed said, nodding to Pam who rushed off to collect it from the office. He quickly looked up the date. 'Yes, I can make that. If that meeting's on the 19th, do I take it that there's little chance of the trial coming up before Christmas?'

'I think it highly improbable. The timing has always been a problem. We applied for an adjournment because we needed time to collect the evidence. Because Dr Dalton's report arrived today, we cannot expect that the case can now suddenly be rushed through.'

'I understand that, Mr Smythe. We just hoped that we'd have our daughter home with us for Christmas.'

'I understand that too, Mr Owen.'

When Ed put the telephone down, there were tears in Sally's eyes. 'So Nicola won't be here for Christmas, Dad?' she asked.

Ed slowly shook his head.

'It's so disappointing,' she sobbed, angrily brushing away her tears. 'So why are we bothering with all these Christmas decorations?'

Putting her arm around her daughter, Pam tried to console her. 'There will be lots of other Christmases, Sally, when we'll all be together. Anyway, Christmas isn't here yet and there's always a chance that Nicola may be released in time.'

'They've got to release her, Mum. They've got to. It's all so unfair. It wasn't her fault,' Sally declared, before bursting into tears once more.

It was not until the next day that any of them could bring themselves to start putting up the Christmas decorations.

By 19 December, almost all the preparations for the Christmas festivities were complete. Both Johnnie and Sally had broken up from school for the holiday. Ed left them helping Pam put the finishing touches to the decorations, when he set off for the conference with Mr Giacomo. He left early, because he wanted first to call on Nicola to break the news, as gently as he could, that the trial would not take place until the New Year.

When he met her, she was in surprisingly high spirits, the happiest he'd seen her for some weeks. He even felt that he could pull her leg about still being a little overweight.

'I know I am, Dad,' she said with a little giggle. 'The trouble is working in the kitchen. Well . . . if you know what I mean, it's all too tempting!'

'It's really good to see you looking so well,' he said, starting the preamble to the bad news he was about to pass on. 'And I'm so sorry that it now looks certain the trial won't—'

Nicola interrupted him. 'I've already been told, Dad,' she said. 'It's all right. We've got lots of things planned here for Christmas and we're all going to have a great time. So don't worry about me. You and Mum enjoy your Christmas with Sally and Johnnie.'

After his unexpectedly pleasant visit, Ed left Holloway for the first and only time with his spirits lifted. He was still in a good mood when, just after five o'clock, he was shown into the barrister's chambers.

Mr Giacomo was sitting at his desk, eating a sandwich. He held out his hand and said, 'Excuse my not getting up.

I'm trying to have the lunch my wife prepared for me. She gets terribly upset if I take it home untouched.'

After Ed had shaken his hand and sat down, Mr Giacomo continued reading the reports in front of him and eating his very late lunch. After crunching away at an apple until it had been reduced to a slim core, he placed it and an uneaten sandwich into a small paper bag. Having wiped his mouth and fingers with a paper serviette, he screwed it into a tiny ball and placed that too in the paper bag. He leaned over and opened the briefcase standing on the floor next to his chair. Carefully, he put the paper bag and its contents into the case and closed it.

Then he looked up and smiled at Ed. 'Well, Mr Owen,' he said, 'I don't have to tell you that this is one hell of a case.'

'I know it is, Mr Giacomo and we're in your hands now.'

'I've just read the medical reports from Dr Wells and Dr Dalton. It's a medical illness without doubt and it can be treated. It's still a bit iffy as to whether Nicola should continue to be treated within a controlled environment. Dr Wells's report is a little more specific on that point than Dr Dalton's. He expressed his willingness to treat Nicola as a non-resident patient at the hospital where he works.'

Ed beamed. 'That's marvellous!' he exclaimed.

'Quite so, Mr Owen. But the reason I wanted to see you is to explain our situation and our problem.'

The gravity of Mr Giacomo's tone alarmed Ed and he felt his stomach muscles suddenly contract.

'It is my intention,' the barrister continued, 'to plead on the grounds of temporary insanity caused by a medical illness which at the time of the arsons had not been diagnosed. That illness is premenstrual syndrome. We can demonstrate that. Moreover, we can prove from Nicola's medical treatment and marked improvement in her behaviour while in prison and the reports now in front of me that the illness can be treated.'

262

'But I don't understand what the problem is,' Ed exclaimed.

'My dear Mr Owen, the problem is this – there is no legal precedent. In plain terms, a case has never been brought before the courts in this country where premenstrual syndrome has been pleaded in defence of a criminal charge. So, whatever the outcome of the case may be, we will be creating legal history.'

Ed didn't have time to digest this before the door of the chamber was quickly opened and the clerk of the chamber came in. 'The Nicola Owen case,' he called to Mr Giacomo. 'It's just come through. We're on tomorrow!'

\*     \*     \*

That evening, I received a Christmas present from my nanny. It was a gold cross and chain. Five minutes later, a wardress came to tell me that I would be going to trial the next day. It was a complete shock. Everybody was excited and congratulated me. My emotions were a mixture of relief that at last a decision was going to be made and fear as to what it might be.

That night I hardly slept. I couldn't even bring myself to think that at the same time the next night I might be in my own bed. It seemed an impossible dream.

Around me was the unrelenting cacophony of sleeping women – grunts and groans and snoring so loud that it even penetrated the pillow I'd pulled over my head. Could it be, could it possibly be that I would never hear it again?

At last, I fell asleep and vivid pictures leap-frogged through my mind – my fire-charred dancing cups and medals, a photograph taken of me at a dance festival being slowly burned as if ignited by a match and then, as though it was a film, me as I was five years before, wearing the costume of the witch and screaming as I was pushed not into the oven but into a gigantic blazing bonfire. Then, as if the camera was quickly zooming out, the witch and the flames became smaller and smaller until I could see them no more.

A hand shaking my shoulder rudely awakened me. The wardress standing by my bed was hissing at me in a loud whisper, 'Come on, Nicola. It's time to get up. You've got to collect all your things together and report to the admissions unit. They'll serve your breakfast down there with the other prisoners who're going out for hearings. Come on now. Shake a leg. They'll start serving breakfast in under half an hour. So don't hang about and make sure you take all your things with you.'

I climbed out of bed and, as all the other women were still fast asleep, I enjoyed the rare privilege of being able to wash in the only wash-basin in the dormitory with at least a semblance of privacy.

A couple of days earlier, Mum had brought in a pretty two-piece outfit in a brown floral print. 'It's for a special occasion,' she'd said. I thought at the time that she'd meant Christmas but, as I was about to set out for the very special occasion of my trial, I put it on and was agreeably pleased with the effect.

It took me a little time to pack the rest of my belongings into a large, white, plastic carrier-bag. I'd only just finished, when the wardress unlocked the door.

'All done, then?' she whispered.

'Yes,' I replied and, with only a most cursory glance around the room, I followed her out towards the admission hall.

'Here we are,' she said at the door.

I half turned to face her. 'I'll say goodbye then.'

She grinned broadly. 'I wouldn't if I were you,' she said. 'You'll probably be back here tonight!'

I heard the door being locked behind me as I walked into the admission hall. There were a couple of dozen other girls there, all chattering, each excited and wondering what the outcome of her appearance in court would be. A few were clearly nervous and didn't eat any of their breakfast, but I tucked in heartily, enjoying my watery porridge, crisply-fried sausage and two thick slices of buttered bread.

The eight of us who were going to the Old Bailey were then escorted to a police van. As it left the prison, the rising sun's pale orange glow was just beginning to light up the December sky.

Around my neck was the gold cross I'd been given by Nanny. I held on to it and silently but earnestly prayed, 'Oh, God, you are the God of love and you know how much I love Mum and Dad and how much they love me. Please, God, allow me to go home to them this day. And this I ask not just for myself but because I cannot bear to cause those I love any more suffering – I know that I'm getting better but, please, please, God, make me well again.'

# CHAPTER TWENTY-TWO

## *The Old Bailey*

There were heavy black rain clouds rolling across the slate grey sky as they headed towards London. Apart from the occasional explosive comment on another motorist's stupidity, Ed drove through the rush-hour traffic in a nervous silence that discouraged conversation.

At last, to break the tension, Pam asked cheerily, 'Which way are you going in, Ed?'

'What a bloody stupid question!' he snapped. 'How many times do I drive to London? And now you want to check my route!'

Pam was unruffled. 'It's only that I heard on the radio that there were problems at the Blackwall Tunnel.'

'I'm not going through that stupid tunnel. There's always problems there. We can't get anything right in this damned country. That tunnel is a bloody disgrace!'

'I was only trying to be helpful, Ed,' Pam said with but a hint of sharpness in her voice.

But it was sufficient for Ed to realize that he was selfishly wallowing in his own fears and worries at a time when, for the sake of the rest of the family, he needed to be strong. 'I'm sorry,' he said contritely. 'I'm being a pig. Just ignore me.'

Sitting in the back seat in the tweed jacket, long skirt and polo-neck sweater that her father had carefully selected for the occasion, Sally exclaimed, 'You're not the only one who feels bad this morning, Dad. We all feel awful. You should think of us as well.'

Pam turned round and, winking at Sally, gently said, 'That's enough, Sally. Your father's very tired, his back is hurting and he's had a lot to do lately.'

'It's all right, Pam,' he said in a more cheerful tone. 'You're right, Sally. I'm fine now.'

He felt anything but. Since the moment he'd been rescued from his disturbed sleep by the ringing of the electric alarm, he'd been edgy. Breakfast had been a sombre affair. Then, like a punctilious drill sergeant, he'd reviewed everybody's dress to make sure it matched his perception of what was appropriate to the occasion. Conscious of every detail, he'd insisted that Johnnie repolished his shoes.

Having crossed Southwark Bridge, Ed was heading towards a car park between Mansion House and the Old Bailey. To get there, he had to negotiate a tricky right turn and then slip left into a small road that would bring him round to the entrance. Unfortunately, he was not in the best approach lane to make the right turn and, as usual in central London, none of the other drivers were willing to give way. Knowing from his experience of continental motoring how intimidating the monstrous bumpers of his Volvo could be, Ed swerved suddenly into his chosen lane to the angry dismay of a fast approaching driver. His extremely vulgar gesture was answered by Ed with a wave, a smile and a mouthed, 'Thank you'.

He made his planned left turn into the narrow road only to discover that it was completely blocked by a refuse lorry with hydraulic lifting gear that massively outpointed the Volvo's bumpers. Ed stopped the car. Nothing seemed to be happening. He looked at his watch. There was still plenty of time but Ed saw no virtue in patience. He sounded the horn. Still nothing seemed to be happening. Pam, who'd been studying the London street map, said, 'You've turned right too early, Ed. I think you should have gone into the one-way system, turned right and then taken the first left.'

Looking at his mirror, Ed saw that another car had stopped behind them. There was no going back. He sounded the horn again. Nothing happened and nobody came. Ed took the book from Pam and checked her map reading. 'Bugger it!' he exclaimed. 'Of course! You're absolutely right!' Seeing that the refuse lorry was parked a little to the right of the road, he made up his mind. 'Sit tight everybody!'

He swung the car up on to the pavement and started to edge forward. The sound of scraping metal confirmed that he'd miscalculated and there was insufficient space for the Volvo between the lorry and the wall.

'Ed, what the hell do you think you're doing?' Pam demanded in astonishment.

'I'll tell you what I'm doing. I'm trying to get to the Old Bailey. That's what I'm doing. What else do you think I'm trying to do?'

'Dad,' Johnnie called from the back seat.

'What is it, Jonathan?'

'You're behaving like a complete wally!'

At that moment, three burly men emerged from an alley, carrying large aluminium bins on their sturdy shoulders. They emptied the bins' contents into the thick metal hopper and the hydraulic arms began to lift upwards. The three men took back the bins and then, for a moment, stood and gazed at the result of Ed's folly. With a knowing shake of their heads, they clambered on the rear duckplate of the lorry as it slowly made its way along the road. Sheepishly, Ed followed.

Finally, after the car had been safely parked, they entered the main hall of the Old Bailey.

'Hello Ed, Pam,' a voice called. 'Hello Sally, Johnnie.'

To their astonishment, it was Peter, the police sergeant whose house flanked their garden. In February, when he'd seen thick black smoke belching out of their house, he'd immediately rushed round. Finding the front door open, he dashed in and, although the fire was raging there, he ran upstairs, determined to ensure that nobody was in any of the five bedrooms. One of these was already a blazing inferno but, with a handkerchief held over his nose and mouth as his only protection from the choking smoke, he quickly checked all the other rooms, each time carefully closing the door behind him. When he was satisfied that there was nobody left in the house, he hurried back downstairs to be met by a fireman who shouted, 'Get out of here. It's going to go any second.'

This remarkable act of bravery by an off-duty policeman was never rewarded or even mentioned in the many press accounts.

'Have you been called as a witness, Peter?' Pam enquired.

He shook his head, 'No, no,' he said and laughed. 'I'm here on security for today.' Seeing their puzzled looks, he explained, 'I'm coming up to retirement and you get duties like this during the run-down period.'

'Well, what a coincidence,' Ed said, 'that you should be here on the day of Nicola's case!'

'It is, isn't it? I saw it listed when I came on duty and thought the same thing. Look, Ed, I know the court you're in. I'll take you there. You'll probably find your barrister has already arrived.' Seeing Ed check his watch, Peter added, 'Don't worry. You've plenty of time.'

Peter led them to where Mr Giacomo was standing outside the door to the court. At his feet was a large bundle of documents tied with pink tape.

'I think these people belong to you, sir,' Peter said with a grin. After greetings had been exchanged, he shook Ed's hand and said, 'Good luck, Ed. I hope it all turns out well for you all.'

'Thank you, Peter. It's helped seeing you here.'

'I'll tell you what. Would you like me to take Johnnie and Sally up to the gallery? I don't think they're allowed in the court proper.'

Mr Giacomo nodded his approval.

'Come on, you two,' Peter said. 'I'll show you upstairs.'

Pam placed a hand on her children's shoulders and, looking earnestly at them, said, 'Please be brave for Nicola's sake. It's not going to be easy and whatever happens you must . . .'

'Don't worry about us, Mum,' Sally interrupted. 'We'll be all right.'

'Everything's going to work out,' Johnnie added. 'You'll see.'

And with that, Peter led them away.

Ed turned to the barrister and asked, 'Is everything ready, Mr Giacomo?'

'It's fine, except I haven't received the report from Nicola's probation officer.'

'Is it important?'

'Yes, it is, Mr Owen. She's an official of the court and her opinions will carry weight.' There was a brief, awkward silence before he said, 'Look, we're on in about twenty minutes. I want to take these documents in and then I must have a word with Nicola. If you and Mrs Owen go up those stairs over there, you'll find a sort of refreshment place where you can have a coffee. OK?'

After Mr Giacomo had entered the court, Ed and Pam stood in silence for some minutes. Neither of them wanted a cup of coffee. They couldn't bear to move away from the place where their daughter would shortly face trial. As Ed stared unseeingly down the long entrance hall, Pam gazed at him. He was anxious and concerned, his back was causing him pain; he was physically and mentally exhausted. She could see the worries and concerns of the past months written over his solemn face. There was nothing more he could do. He'd played his vital part in trying to save their daughter. The trial would be the culmination of his untiring efforts, his refusal to be intimidated by either doctors or lawyers. He wasn't the most romantic man in the world and, God knows, he had his faults, but she loved him for what he was – a fighter who would never stop fighting for what he believed was right and fighting for those he loved, for his children and for her.

'Come on, Ed,' she said, taking his arm. 'Let's go in and sit down.'

As they walked towards the door, a round-faced man with grey hair stopped them and said, 'Mr and Mrs Owen?'

'Yes?' Ed replied questioningly.

'I'm Charles Flower. I'm a probation officer at the Old Bailey.'

As they shook hands with him, both Ed and Pam were puzzled to know why they'd been accosted by this grey-suited official.

'Were you about to go in?' he enquired.

'Yes. We thought we should get ourselves used to the atmosphere before the proceedings begin,' Ed replied.

'Do you mind if I sit with you? I'm interested to hear your daughter's case.'

Although this too puzzled them, Ed and Pam readily agreed.

When they were seated, Mr Flower said, 'It's a most interesting case. I'm so pleased you've discovered that Nicola's illness can be treated.'

'Thank you,' Pam replied. 'We can only hope the judge sees it that way.'

Mr Flower nodded and said, 'Certainly the judge who will hear the case is a very able man.'

'But is he a good man, or rather, a good judge?' Ed enquired.

'He is a very experienced judge and, I believe, he's a very understanding man.'

'I do hope you're right,' Pam said softly. 'We shall need all the understanding we can get.'

Once again, Mr Flower nodded and then, folding his arms across his chest, said, 'You see, I used to suffer from a mild form of epilepsy. It was ruining my life but then they discovered what was wrong and gave me a pill.

271

I take just one a day and I live a perfectly normal life. It's marvellous what can be done these days.'

Neither Ed nor Pam really knew why they were being told this, but they were pleased to be with somebody who seemed so sympathetic.

'Nicola has to take a pill,' Pam said, 'but only for a certain number of days.'

Mr Flower nodded and said, 'Yes, I know.'

That he knew so much puzzled them even more.

\*　　\*　　\*

I'd been left to wait for hours in a small, brightly lit cell beneath the Old Bailey. I could not stop worrying about what the outcome would be. At my last trial there, I'd been able to walk out of the front door with my parents. Could that possibly happen a second time? It seemed too much to hope for.

When Mr Giacomo arrived, he did nothing to boost my confidence. 'I want to make this crystal clear to you, Nicola,' he said. 'We're going to enter a plea of "guilty as charged". Your defence is one of temporary insanity at the time of both arsons.' I tried to speak, but he waved his hand impatiently and went on. 'We haven't much time and I must say this. If the judge doesn't accept what I say, you could be given a prison sentence of up to twelve years.'

'Oh, my God!' I gasped in absolute terror. I'd had no idea the sentence could be so harsh. Probably to stop me worrying, Mr Giacomo had only ever suggested a sentence of, at most, eighteen months.

'Arson is a serious offence, Nicola, and it is an offence that you have twice committed. If the judge gives you a sentence of more than three years, we shall appeal. I consider that anything less than three years is acceptable. But I do have some good news. I've just been handed the report from your probation officer and it's very good indeed.' He stood up, gently squeezed my arm and said, 'I'll see you in the court.'

Confusion spun through my brain. I thought it had been discovered that I had a hormone imbalance that could be dealt with and yet my barrister was saying that I would possibly have to serve a long prison sentence. What kind of cure was that? I'd already been in prison for over five months. Hadn't I been punished enough?

I heard my name being called. The cell door was swung open and I was escorted up the back stairs. I then had to wait outside the court. The uniformed wardress opened the door a little and I was able to look around. First, I saw my brother and sister in the gallery. I waved at them and they smiled back. I felt so upset that I couldn't just go over to them and hold them. Then I saw my mother and father sitting in the body of the court. They both looked very nervous and worried, but they waved to me.

At a table at the front of the court, Mr Giacomo was shuffling through his papers. Sitting behind another much larger table was quite a large group of people who were chatting away to each other.

'Who are they?' I whispered to the wardress.

'That's the press,' she replied. 'Looks as though you've caught the attention of the reporters.'

A gavel was struck loudly three times and everybody in court stopped talking.

A voice said, 'The court will rise,' and everybody in court stood up.

'*Regina* versus Nicola Owen.'

To the left of the court, a door opened and the judge entered. He was very slim and tall. He walked purposefully to the central raised dais where he sat down in his high-backed chair.

'Bring in the prisoner.'

The wardress pushed the door fully open and I was led into the dock, a small area, boxed in with high wooden panels. The wardress sat down just behind me.

The judge beckoned Mr Giacomo to him and they exchanged some quiet words, occasionally looking across at an empty table. The judge then turned and peered over the top of his spectacles at the clock above the door through which he'd entered.

Everybody waited in silence.

As I was watching the judge, I noticed that he seemed to be staring intently at where I knew my mother and father were sitting. Then, for a disconcerting moment, he stared searchingly at me.

On the press benches, the reporters had started fidgeting and whispering to each other. Suddenly, the judge leaned over his desk and said something to the clerk, who rapped his gavel down on its polished wood base. Once again, everybody was silent.

'Mr Giacomo,' the judge said, 'I am advised that prosecuting counsel and the police witnesses are delayed in the Blackwall Tunnel.' He glanced again at the clock before continuing. 'It's ten twenty-five now and I propose to adjourn until eleven o'clock.'

There was another loud clack of the gavel and the clerk announced, 'The court is adjourned until eleven o'clock. The court will rise.'

We all stood up in unison and watched silently as the judge closed the file in front of him and, having tucked it securely under his arm, started walking towards the door. Suddenly he stopped and turned to Mr Giacomo. Pointing to the bulky file, he said, 'It's fascinating, absolutely fascinating. Premenstrual syndrome indeed.' Then, having glanced at me, he said, 'When this court reconvenes, I see no reason why the young lady should return to the dock. Let her come and sit in the well of the court.' With that, he walked out of the door.

I was led back downstairs for half an hour. It was the longest half-hour of my life.

★　　★　　★

His face flushed with excitement, Mr Giacomo bounded across the court to Ed and Pam. 'Did you hear that?' he exclaimed. 'Did you hear what he said?'

'But what does it mean?' Ed asked.

'I don't know what it means for sure, Mr Owen, but in all the years I've been at the bar I've never heard or seen anything like it.' He beamed with excitement. 'It's got to be regarded as . . .' For a moment, words failed him. 'It must be a good indication. Come on! Let's go and have some coffee while we still have time.'

Somewhat bemused, Ed and Pam went to the refreshment area, collected their coffees and joined a jubilant-looking Mr Giacomo at a table.

'I heard on the radio there was some trouble at the Blackwall Tunnel,' Pam said. 'I mentioned it to Ed.'

'Which way did you come, Mr Owen?'

'Over Southwark Bridge,' he replied.

'And via the side of a refuse lorry,' Pam added.

Her account of Ed's misadventure greatly amused Mr Giacomo, but it was what happened in court that he really wanted to talk about. 'I'm sure this adjournment will help us. I should think the judge will use the time to read the file, or at least enough of it to give him a clear idea of what has taken place over these last few months.'

At this point, two policemen came in. Both Ed and Pam recognized one of them. 'Aren't you . . .?' Ed said and stopped, having completely forgotten the name.

'Sergeant Unwin. Hello, Mr Owen. Hello, Mrs Owen.'

The two, it emerged, were the police witnesses for the prosecution who had been delayed at the Blackwall Tunnel.

A little while later, they all left together and went down to the court. Standing beside the door was a barrister whom Sergeant Unwin introduced to the Owens as being the prosecuting counsel. Looking with some puzzlement at Pam, she said, 'I know you, don't I?'

'Beaverwood Grammar School?' Pam asked. 'You're Daphne Turner, aren't you?'

The prosecuting counsel nodded. 'And your name's Pam Standfast, isn't it?'

'Pam Owen now.'

'You're not Nicola Owen's . . .?'

'Yes, I am and this is my husband.'

'Good gracious me!' She shook her head in disbelief. Then nodding towards the door, she said, 'Well, I think we should all go in now.'

As they re-entered the court, Ed suddenly realized that he had quite forgotten about Sally and Johnnie. Feeling a qualm of guilt, he walked towards the front of the court room to have a clear view of the gallery. They were both still sitting there, looking extremely bored. When they saw him, they grimaced rather than smiled. Aware that as an apology it was less than adequate, he mouthed the words, 'I'm very sorry.'

The gavel sounded before he'd regained his seat and the procedures for calling the court to order began again. As he and Pam sat down, Mr Flower slipped back into his place beside them.

Nicola and the accompanying wardress were shown to chairs in the well of the court. Having called the prisoner to stand, the clerk read the details of the three charges – arson, endangering life and intent to kill. Nicola pleaded guilty to the first two and not guilty to intent to kill.

Miss Turner, prosecuting counsel, stood up and the judge nodded his assent for her to begin.

'I would advise my lord,' she announced, 'that the police are not pursuing the third charge – intent to kill.'

The judge turned to Mr Giacomo and asked, 'Do you wish to make any comment on that at this stage?'

After Mr Giacomo had replied that he was aware of the circumstances and appreciated why the charge had been withdrawn, the judge asked prosecuting counsel to continue. She did so by calling the first witness.

As Sergeant Unwin was sworn in, the judge studied him judiciously. Then he said, 'Sergeant Unwin, I have your statement here before me and I have read it carefully. Do you wish to add to or amend this statement?'

'No, my lord.'

'Nothing whatever?'

'That is correct, my lord.'

'Do I understand correctly that the police are fully satisfied that the arson was not committed by the accused with the deliberate intention of killing her mother?'

'That is correct, my lord.'

'Nor with the deliberate intention of killing any other person?'

'That is correct, my lord.'

Turning to prosecuting counsel, the judge asked, 'The prisoner has pleaded guilty to the two charges. Are there any further aspects that you wish to bring to my attention?'

'I would like to draw your lordship's attention to an earlier arson which—'

'I am aware of that information.'

'Then there are no further aspects.'

'Thank you, counsel. Unless, Mr Giacomo, you have any questions to put to the witness, I propose asking him to stand down.'

'Thank you, my lord. I have no questions for the witness.'

Looking rather puzzled, Sergeant Unwin left the stand.

'Mr Giacomo, I would like your help in this,' the judge said. 'Let me explain my understanding of your written submission and perhaps you can then comment. The accused has in fact pleaded guilty to the charge of arson and to the charge of endangering life as a result of that arson. Your submission is that the accused cannot be held responsible for her actions at that time because she was suffering from a severe mental disorder. This mental disorder was not psychiatric but had as its cause a medical illness that had not been diagnosed as such at the time when the offences were committed. This medical illness has subsequently been diagnosed and is susceptible to treatment. This illness is described as premenstrual syndrome. Am I correct?'

'You are correct, my lord, thus far.'

'In support of your submission, you have produced the reports of both Dr Wells, the Chief Psychiatrist of Holloway Prison, who has been giving medical treatment to the accused, and of Dr Dalton, who is a specialist in the field of premenstrual syndrome. Am I correct thus far, Mr Giacomo?'

'You are correct, my lord.'

'Dr Wells's report refers to the accused's bizarre, exotic and antisocial behaviour before the administration of the treatment. This treatment, administered under his supervision, has been that of an oral . . .' He paused to peer through his spectacles at the notes in front of him. '. . . an oral dydroprogesterone, which is a synthetic preparation similar to a hormone called progesterone. Have I understood that correctly, Mr Giacomo?'

'You have understood correctly, my lord.'

'Dr Wells's report goes on to state that, since the administration of this hormone, the accused's behaviour has normalized. The report of Dr Dalton, the expert in this particular field, confirms that this treatment, if modified according to circumstances, will ensure continuation of her normal behaviour. Is that not so?'

'That is so, my lord.'

The judge sat back in his chair with both arms stretched out before him to allow a finger on each hand simultaneously to tap the bench on either side of the open file. Then he continued, 'Mr Giacomo, is there anything you wish to add or bring to the attention of this court?'

'No, my lord. I have nothing further to add.'

By this time, the judge's spectacles were precariously balanced on the end of his nose. He stared over them and said, 'Unless prosecuting counsel has any points to raise, I am minded to reach a conclusion to this case.'

Miss Turner stood up and said, 'We are content, my lord.'

'Thank you, counsel,' the judge said. He then asked both defence and prosecution counsels to refer to a specific document. 'This is a letter,' he went on, 'dated the 14 November this year from Dr Morley to the defendant's solicitor. It is headed, "Nicola Jane Owen".' He paused until he was sure that both counsels had found the letter. Then he said, 'I refer to paragraph six that begins towards the bottom of page one and continues on to the second page.' He waited again until he was satisfied that the paragraph had been identified. 'Dr Morley is well known to this court,' he continued, 'and his opinions are greatly respected. In this letter, at the commencement of paragraph six, he says this and I quote: "I am too long in the tooth to be over-impressed with miracles." ' The judge stopped again and sat back in his chair. Removing his spectacles, he waved them slowly at the court as he asked, 'Why would Dr Morley write that?'

Nobody in the court answered. Nor did it seem as though the judge expected a response. The silence in the solemn courtroom seemed to intensify as everybody waited for the judge to continue.

'The reason why Dr Morley wrote that,' he said at last, 'was because what he had seen was, in fact, a miracle. Yes, a miracle! That is precisely what he had seen.'

There was not a movement or a sound, not even a gasp in the court as all eyes were fixed on the learned judge.

He sat upright, placed his spectacles full on his nose, looked straight at Nicola and, slowly and very deliberately, said, 'The court's sole concern is to help you. Doctors have recently given you the most spectacular treatment and that has resulted in you being able to cope with your menstrual functions in a way that does not involve the bizarre behaviour which previously occurred, due entirely to chemical deficiencies in your body. Nicola Jane Owen, you may go free from this court!'

Despite the historic nature of the judgement, there was no cheering or clapping as there might have been in a film. Everybody remained totally silent as the judge stood up and turned to leave. He stopped, looked across at Nicola, and said, 'And a very happy Christmas to you and your family.' Then he left the court, still stunned into silence.

As soon as the judge had gone, Nicola rushed across the court and into her mother's arms. They clung to each other, both sobbing with joy.

Mr Giacomo hurried up to Ed and breathlessly said, 'I know, it's marvellous, but he got carried away. She pleaded guilty and he hasn't dealt with the probationary order. I have to go straight away to his chambers to have the formalities properly completed.'

Still locked in her mother's embrace, Nicola looked up and cried, 'Dad! Oh Dad!'

Ed stepped forward and put his arms around his wife and his daughter. 'Oh, my Nicola! Isn't it just marvellous?' he said and kissed them both.

As Mr Giacomo was about to leave the court room, the door opened and a herd of reporters charged in, pushing him against the wall. There was so much shouting that it was impossible to hear what he said in answer to their flurry of questions.

Through the bobbing heads that filled the doorway, Ed could just see Sally and Johnnie trying to force their way in. He stepped forward, wanting desperately to unite them with the family.

It was at this opportune moment that Mr Flower took over. 'Follow me,' he said. As he reached the crush, he shouted authoratively, 'Make way, please. I'm an officer of the court.'

Instantly, a pathway cleared and Ed, holding grimly on to Nicola and Pam, followed in Mr Flower's wake out into the hall where Sally and Johnnie grabbed hold of Nicola and kissed her. But there was no time for them to say anything.

280

'Come with me,' Mr Flower said urgently. 'We must go now!'

They walked quickly behind him until they were safely inside his office.

'It'll be better to stay here for a while,' he said. 'Otherwise, you'll be mobbed by reporters.' He went over to the windows and closed the blinds. A gap was left in one of them and, almost immediately, a man was there, peering in. Mr Flower moved across and stood against the window so that his back was blocking the view.

Too dazed to speak, the Owen family huddled in a group, clutching on to each other as though some unexpected force might yet drag them apart.

'I have a plan,' Mr Flower announced. 'I'll take you all out through the back way. Do you have a car here, Mr Owen?'

Ed nodded and described where his car was parked.

'That's good. The car park entrance almost faces the back door of this building. We'll go down there and I'll let you out on your own, Mr Owen. Collect the car, drive outside and unlock the car doors, but stay in the car and keep the engine running. I shall be looking out for you and, as soon as you arrive, I'll open the door to let your family come out. You must all move fast and get in the car as quickly as you can. Then you mustn't hang about, Mr Owen. As soon as they're in the car, drive off.' He then asked Nicola if she had anything to collect.

'Just one plastic bag with all my things in it.'

'I'll go and collect it. I won't be more than a few minutes.'

Left alone, the Owens tried their best to ignore the inquisitive faces peering through the gap in the blind.

Mr Flower soon returned with Nicola's bag and said, 'Right. Here we go! Follow me!' He led the way through a maze of passages and long silent corridors. Eventually, they stopped in front of a heavy door. Mr Flower took a key from his pocket and unlocked it. Opening it slightly, he peered outside. 'All right, Mr Owen,' he said. 'The coast seems clear.'

Ed left, walking casually for a while and then breaking into a brisk run that didn't stop until he reached the car. Wasting no time, he drove it to just outside the door. As it opened and his family came running out, they were immediately seen by two photographers who started sprinting towards them. As Ed shouted at them to hurry, Pam and the three children piled into the car and, even before they'd slammed the doors, Ed accelerated away, managing to avoid knocking down the two photographers who, in a last ditch attempt to halt the escape, had stood in the middle of the road.

The family, reunited at last, drove home in time for Christmas.

# Epilogue

Newspapers treated my trial as a big Christmas story and my parents received a mass of mail, much of it from the parents of teenage girls whose behavioural problems seemed similar to my own. One of the most welcome letters was sent to Mr Smythe, our solicitor, by Dr Morley, who once had been so insistent that it was best for me to be treated in Broadmoor. His letter said: 'I was most gratified to read in the press the result of Nicola Owen's trial. I can only hope that the diagnosis and optimism prove to be justified. Would you kindly convey my congratulations to Mr and Mrs Owen. Their devotion to their daughter and their determination not to give up was an object lesson to us all.'

Dr Morley's note of caution found no place in the press reports which, echoing the judge's words, universally claimed that I'd been given a magic cure while I was in prison. In fact, my release from Holloway was the start of a long journey along the road to normality. My confidence was in tatters and emotionally I had missed out on the very important adolescent years. Although I lived outwardly as an adult in an adult world, I was still inwardly immature and it took several years for me to attain emotional maturity. To make matters worse, I had a criminal record so that in any new social or work situation I had to account in some way for those lost years.

My visits to Dr Dalton were very frequent at first when my treatment had to be stabilized and focused on my particular needs. Because of the severity of my hormone imbalance, I was eventually given a daily injection of progesterone and an implant into my stomach every three to six months. I made the decision to inject myself so that I wasn't restricted by the work schedule of the local district nurse.

Progesterone is a thick fluid and the needle used for the injection is one and a half inches long. On the first occasion I had to inject myself, I spent two hours plucking up the courage to jab the needle in! Today, it is almost as routine as cleaning my teeth.

The first inputs of progesterone made me feel so much brighter, but did nothing to remove the great sense of guilt and remorse I felt for the worry and concern I'd caused my family. In the early days, the psychological effect of what I had been through left me with a low self-esteem and little self-worth.

I knew that I had to start working and my first job was as a barmaid. This forced me to meet people and did wonders in rehabilitating me into society and rebuilding my shattered self-confidence. After about a year, I moved on and obtained a position as a sales assistant working within a department store. After nine months there, I was promoted to department manageress.

Because of the trauma and wasted years experienced as a teenager, I was determined to prove myself. Now I am proud to own a small but successful company that boasts an impressive list of major customers. It is hard but rewarding work that satisfies my creative instincts.

My relationship with my brother and sister has improved with each passing year. They quickly ceased to feel embarrassed and their trust in me grew as I progressed in my working life. For the first time in many years, we rediscovered the genuine affection and close friendship we felt towards each other. Now we are extremely close and I am as proud of their successes as they are of mine. Sally is a dynamic and much-travelled night-club singer and pianist. Johnnie is happily married and works for my father's company.

My parents have moved away from Camden Road and tried to put thoughts of what went on there behind them. They naturally continued to worry about me for some time and were at first inclined to be over-protective. But as I grew into maturity, I began to understand and appreciate the wonderful gift they had given me. Without their unfaltering love, I would not be here today and I am eternally grateful to them.

I can remember when I was in Holloway Prison that I wrote to Dad asking why God was making me suffer so much. I shall never forget his reply. 'Nicola,' he wrote, 'if we didn't have ugliness in the world how could we appreciate beauty? If there wasn't sickness, how could we appreciate our health? If we didn't suffer bad times, how could we really appreciate the good times in our lives? One day, you will look back on this terrible time and discover another truth – that something good always comes out of something bad.'

Years later, I realized what good had emerged. Before my illness, I took so much for granted. I was, perhaps, a little superficial and unaware of life's true values. The fight back to living a normal life has, I feel, given me an inner strength and made me a better and a stronger person than I would otherwise have been.

For many years, I was often thought to be cold and without feeling. I suppose this was my way of protecting myself from emotional hurt and pain. Although I had boyfriends, there was always something lacking in the relationship and I preferred to remain independent, free from emotional commitment. But, deep down, I longed for something more, even though I didn't believe I would ever find it.

But I did. In the autumn of 1990 I fell in love for the first time in my life with a man who, incredibly, felt the same way about me. Mum had always told me that when I met the right person, I'd just know. Well, I did know and, in December 1991, Guy and I were married. Now I feel so confident that my life has finally and completely come together.

One day, I hope that Guy and I will have children. My greatest wish is that we will give to them the same unconditional love my parents gave to me.

**Should you require any information regarding PMS, then please write to:**

**PMS Help
PO Box 160
St Albans
Herts AL1 4UQ**

# 'Steps To Freedom'

Introduced by Jeni Barnett, this informative and entertaining video programme shows how you can overcome mild to moderate Premenstrual Syndrome by changing the way you eat.

We talk to women, including Nicola Owen, who have benefited from this advice. In a series of easy steps we show how you can chart your symptoms and help yourself to beat PMS.

Please enclose a cheque/postal order for £11.49 (£9.99 + £1.50 p&p) made payable to PMS Help, PO Box 160, St Albans, Herts AL1 4UQ.

NAME (Block Letters) ...............................................

ADDRESS ...............................................................

............................................................................

POSTAL CODE .....................................................

PMS Help is a registered charity No 1005455

# A SELECTION OF BIOGRAPHIES
# FROM CORGI AND BLACK SWAN

THE PRICES SHOWN BELOW WERE CORRECT AT THE TIME OF GOING TO PRESS. HOWEVER TRANSWORLD PUBLISHERS RESERVE THE RIGHT TO SHOW NEW RETAIL PRICES ON COVERS WHICH MAY DIFFER FROM THOSE PREVIOUSLY ADVERTISED IN THE TEXT OR ELSEWHERE.

| | | | | | |
|---|---|---|---|---|---|
| ☐ | 13582 8 | The God Squad | *Paddy Doyle* | £4.99 |
| ☐ | 13928 9 | Daughter of Persia | *S. Farman Farmaian* | £5.99 |
| ☐ | 13669 7 | Dangerous Candy | *Rafaella Fletcher* | £2.99 |
| ☐ | 13587 9 | Every Letter Counts | *Susan Hampshire* | £3.99 |
| ☐ | 99505 3 | Truth to Tell | *Ludovic Kennedy* | £7.99 |
| ☐ | 13892 4 | Fifty Years in the System | *Jimmy Laing* | £5.99 |
| ☐ | 13550 X | Diana's Story | *Deric Longden* | £3.99 |
| ☐ | 13769 3 | Lost for Words | *Deric Longden* | £3.99 |
| ☐ | 13356 6 | Not Without My Daughter | *Betty Mahmoody* | £4.99 |
| ☐ | 99509 6 | Martha Jane and Me | *Mavis Nicholson* | £5.99 |
| ☐ | 13824 X | Just Some Stories for Eleanor | *Stephen Pegg* | £3.99 |
| ☐ | 99533 9 | Grotesque Libels | *Adam Raphael* | £5.99 |
| ☐ | 13369 8 | Revolution from Within | *Gloria Steinem* | £5.99 |
| ☐ | 13732 4 | A Mother's War | *Fey von Hassell* | £4.99 |
| ☐ | 99512 6 | Nobody Nowhere | *Donna Williams* | £5.99 |

All Corgi/Black Swan Books are available at your bookshop or newsagent, or can be ordered from the following address:
Corgi/Bantam Books,
Cash Sales Department,
P.O. Box 11, Falmouth, Cornwall TR10 9EN

UK and B.F.P.O. customers please send a cheque or postal order (no currency) and allow £1.00 for postage and packing for the first book plus 50p for the second book and 30p for each additional book to a maximum charge of £3.00 (7 books plus).

Overseas customers, including Eire, please allow £2.00 for postage and packing for the first book plus £1.00 for the second book and 50p for each subsequent title ordered.

NAME (Block Letters) ..................................................................................

ADDRESS ..................................................................................................

..............................................................................................................